How to Be a Nurse Assistant Workbook

A Quality Approach to Long Term Care

Julie Gdowski, RN

AHCA®

AMERICAN HEALTH CARE ASSOCIATION

Author/Editor
Julie Gdowski, RN

Designer
Merrifield Graphics & Publishing Service

Cover Designer
Chip Henderson

Cover Photographer
Transcending Dreams Photography

Cover Model
Devin Tucker

Photography & Illustrations
Shutterstock
Imagineeringart.com Inc.

Proofreader
Melissa Rogers

Chief Operating Officer/Senior Vice President, Member Relations
Jennifer Shimer

Marketing and Marketing Research Vice President
Jon-Patrick Ewing

Marketing Director
Chip Henderson

Project Managers
Jon-Patrick Ewing and Chip Henderson

Sales/Customer Service
Lisa Hohenemser

Printer
ASAPfast!

EIGHTH EDITION

ISBN 978-1-7923-9581-9

PRINTED IN THE UNITED STATES

Notice to Readers
Great effort has been taken to confirm the accuracy of the information presented and to describe generally accepted practices. However, the author, editors, and publisher are not responsible for errors or omissions or for any consequences from application of the information in this book and make no warranty, expressed or implied, with respect to the currency, completeness, or accuracy of the contents of the publication. Application of this information in a particular situation remains the professional responsibility of the practitioner; the clinical treatments described and recommended may not be considered absolute and universal recommendations.

Ordering Information
How to Be a Nurse Assistant Workbook can be ordered directly from the American Health Care Association. Special discounts are available for quantity purchases.

web: ahcapublications.org
phone: 800-321-0343
email: publications@ahca.org

To the Student

This workbook is designed to be a study guide to help you learn the material you are reading in **How to Be a Nurse Assistant**. Be sure to read the chapters in the textbook before trying to complete the exercises in this workbook.

The textbook and workbook are closely linked; therefore, it is important for you to refer to the textbook as you complete each exercise. Unless your instructor suggests a different approach, work through the chapters in the workbook shortly after reading the matching chapter in the textbook. Answers to the exercises are on the instructor's website.

A variety of exercises have been included in this workbook with the goal of appealing to your individual learning style. Formats include:

- Crossword Puzzle
- Work Search
- Fill in the Blank
- Labeling
- Matching
- Multiple Choice
- Spell It Out
- True/False

Initial activities in each chapter, such a crossword puzzles, fill in the blank, matching, and spell it out will call upon your ability to find, recall, and be familiar with medical and key terms. True/false, multiple choice, and content review questions will help you grasp concepts, relationships, and rules. Labeling activities encourage you to recognize and relate pictures to words. Additional matching activities encourage you to think critically and decide how to handle realistic situations a nurse assistant will face. You will have the opportunity to prioritize activities, choose how to react to a difficult situation, or decide what to say to a resident or family member at an awkward moment.

Take the practice exams to help you prepare for the written portion of the state competency test. The competency checklists at the back of the book will help guide you through successful completion of all direct care procedures described in the textbook.

Remember that the activities in the workbook do not intend to "test" you but to support what you will learn from the textbook and in class. Have fun with these exercises, remember to refer to your textbook when necessary, and ask your instructor for help with any questions you can't answer.

Completing these exercises will better prepare you for completion of the training, successful completion of the state competency exam, and for your role as a nurse assistant.

Contents

Your Health Care Career

Activity 1: Crossword

Terms to Know

Administrator
Care plan
Charge nurse
Gerontology
Grooming
Long term care
Medicaid
Medical Director
Medicare
Nutrition
Physical therapist
Rehabilitation
Resident
Shift

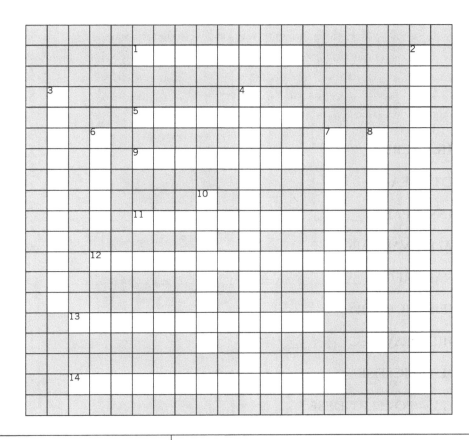

Across

1 Joint federal-state health insurance program for low-income individuals and families

5 Person admitted to a long term care facility

9 Hair and nail care

11 Written document created after the resident assessment that outlines the goals of care, nursing interventions (actions and approaches), and the time frame for accomplishment and evaluation

12 Care designed to help residents return to a previous level of physical functioning after an illness or injury

13 Health care or personal care services that are provided for an extended period of time

14 Manages the facility and directs all staff

Down

2 Provides rehabilitation services to improve resident's physical abilities

3 The study of aging adults and the process of aging

4 In charge of general medical care

6 Scheduled period of work

7 Nourishment for the body provided by food and drink

8 Gives the specific care assignments to nursing staff and has the day-to-day responsibility for supervising resident care

10 Federal health insurance program for individuals age 65 and older and certain people with disabilities

AMERICAN HEALTH CARE ASSOCIATION

Activity 2: Word Scramble

Services Offered in LTC Facilities

Unscramble each term, and spell it correctly in the space provided.

Dental care   Diagnostic imaging services   Dietary plans   Dining
Medical care   Nursing care   Occupational therapy   Personal care
Pharmaceutical   Quality-of-life needs   Rehabilitative care   Recreational therapy
Residential care   Restorative care   Social activities   Social workers
Speech therapy   Spiritual services

1. ECDMILA ACRE _____

2. LENADT RCEA _____

3. URGNNSI CEAR _____

4. IRETIALEIHVABT ARCE _____

5. OSPLNARE RECA _____

6. SRTDIEIEANL CEAR _____

7. APURIILTS IRSVESEC _____

8. ACISOL TVAICITISE _____

9. TQAIYLU – FO-IELF NDESE _____

10. NGIIDN _____

11. AEDITYR LASPN _____

12. AUTCIPMAELHACR _____

13. CAGTNIIODS MINIGGA VSRSECIE _____

14. AINCLREATORE YAETRHP _____

15. EHSPCE RPHAEYT _____

16. SCOAIL ESWRRKO _____

17. ORAVREESTTI RCAE _____

18. ICULNOAPCOAT YAEPRTH _____

Activity 3: Matching
The Interdisciplinary Team

Match the description to the job title of the team member.

1. _____ Plans and directs activities for residents that help improve quality of life

2. _____ Helps residents maintain or improve their physical abilities, such as posture, walking, and range of movement

3. _____ Plans meals and designs special diets to ensure good nutrition for residents

4. _____ Coordinates religious services and provides counseling for residents and family members

5. _____ Staff physician is in charge of general medical care and may provide direct care to residents

6. _____ Focus on improving residents' abilities to perform everyday tasks

7. _____ Includes registered nurses, licensed practical nurses, and nurse assistants

8. _____ Give the specific care assignments to nursing staff

9. _____ Supervises the nursing staff and establishes the philosophy and approach for caregiving

10. _____ Counsels residents and their families and might also arrange home care services for residents who are being discharged

11. _____ Works with residents who have difficulty speaking or swallowing improve speech and language abilities

12. _____ Helps residents through the admission process

13. _____ Manages the facility and directs all staff

14. _____ Person receiving care

A. Nursing staff

B. Physical therapist

C. Activities director

D. Director of Nursing

E. Speech-language pathologist

F. Occupational therapist

G. Admissions director

H. Administrator

I. Charge nurse

J. Resident

K. Social worker

L. Spiritual counselor

M. Registered dietician

N. Medical director

Activity 4: Word Search

How Nurse Assistants Help Residents

```
X  I  G  M  W  A  E  I  I  C  J  N  F  G  N  I  T  E  L  I  O  T  G  N
S  A  P  B  C  Z  D  L  G  T  U  F  M  Q  X  D  Z  A  Z  C  R  G  N  H
E  Y  V  N  Z  F  P  S  S  R  T  O  P  A  M  J  X  T  W  T  A  N  I  N
S  B  R  U  B  O  I  L  M  A  Q  S  R  T  K  W  R  O  L  J  Z  I  K  O
I  J  K  E  C  M  T  A  G  N  X  P  X  Y  Z  I  C  C  G  Z  S  S  L  I
C  H  F  E  O  R  H  E  H  S  R  E  D  A  S  O  N  O  H  S  L  S  A  T
R  D  W  R  O  N  Z  M  T  F  G  N  Z  Q  H  C  Y  G  V  Y  B  E  W  A
E  P  T  A  L  K  I  N  G  E  N  T  Y  T  N  Y  P  V  T  X  N  R  A  R
X  X  U  C  F  T  O  W  N  R  I  G  A  R  E  Q  E  X  B  H  F  D  Q  D
E  G  N  L  I  R  O  K  H  S  M  H  M  Z  U  R  S  G  P  T  E  B  D  Y
N  E  D  I  B  O  H  P  F  E  O  U  S  C  V  O  S  N  T  K  D  B  Q  H
O  K  R  A  A  P  R  A  A  X  O  W  U  V  D  K  I  K  A  A  T  M  E  B
I  Y  E  N  T  P  Z  M  Z  R  R  H  H  P  Z  K  I  V  C  C  C  I  M  D
T  G  S  D  H  U  G  E  R  O  G  P  F  U  H  N  M  Y  I  A  E  R  O  U
O  I  S  N  I  S  U  F  G  N  I  N  E  T  S  I  L  W  X  Q  N  B  N  K
M  O  I  A  N  L  R  Y  K  I  R  D  X  L  V  B  V  D  B  U  S  S  V  F
F  P  N  R  G  A  G  U  O  P  H  Y  S  I  C  A  L  C  O  M  F  O  R  T
O  A  G  I  K  N  T  R  O  F  M  O  C  G  N  I  D  I  V  O  R  P  W  G
E  U  D  A  C  O  P  O  S  I  T  I  O  N  I  N  G  F  B  Q  E  O  U  O
G  C  U  H  R  I  W  L  O  R  T  N  O  C  N  O  I  T  C  E  F  N  I  M
N  S  S  U  A  T  P  M  B  U  X  L  W  X  C  N  C  Y  S  V  X  H  P  X
A  O  V  P  D  O  G  S  I  J  O  R  A  L  H  Y  G  I  E  N  E  G  R  V
R  D  A  L  N  M  C  J  W  Z  H  I  E  J  E  X  Q  H  S  S  F  R  S  R
H  A  W  I  M  E  V  E  X  E  R  B  K  N  M  B  O  H  Q  V  R  V  K  U
```

Transfers	Grooming	Emotional support
Physical comfort	Infection control	Listening
Positioning	Walking	Talking
Providing comfort	Toileting	Snacks
Making the bed	Range of motion exercises	Undressing
Hair and nail care	Oral hygiene	Meals
Hydration	Dressing	Bathing

Activity 5: True or False

Beside each statement, write T for TRUE or F for FALSE.

1. _____ Everyone believes life is worth living as long as they have enough money.

2. _____ Life ends when a person enters long term care.

3. _____ The resident's care plan is used daily by the interdisciplinary care team.

4. _____ The social worker is usually responsible for admitting a new resident.

5. _____ Paying for long term care is often a challenge for residents and their families.

6. _____ Medicaid pays for long-term costs for people with limited income.

7. _____ All long term care facilities provide dietary and pharmacy services.

8. _____ CMS requires long term care facilities to follow government rules and regulations.

9. _____ Long term care facilities are surveyed by the states every five years.

10. _____ All long term care facilities are accredited by JCAHO.

Activity 6: Multiple Choice
Taking Care of You

Circle the letter beside the correct answer.

1. What is a key component to being efficient?
   A. Skipping the less important tasks.
   B. Managing your time.
   C. Doing only the things that matter to you.
   D. Rushing.

2. Which response is NOT a time management strategy?
   A. Prioritize your tasks.
   B. Don't let the residents have a say.
   C. Learn the best ways to perform your tasks.
   D. Take control of your tasks.

3. Which of the following promotes a healthy lifestyle?
   A. Having a positive attitude.
   B. Getting regular exercise.
   C. Eating a variety of healthy foods in appropriate amounts.
   D. All of the above.

4. What is one way to develop a positive attitude?
   A. Drive an expensive car to work.
   B. Don't do tasks that you don't enjoy.
   C. Every day, remember that you make a difference in other's lives.
   D. Watch your favorite TV program at work so you don't get bored.

5. What is NOT an effective way to manage stress?
   A. Getting adequate sleep.
   B. Drinking diet soda.
   C. Practicing yoga and meditation.
   D. Spending time with friends.

Activity 7: In Your Own Words

Describe what makes life worth living for you.

1. Imagine what it must be like to live in a long term care facility.

_____

_____

_____

_____

_____

_____

_____

2. Make a list of things you would like to continue to do if you were a resident in a long term care facility.

_____

_____

_____

_____

_____

_____

_____

Communication and Customer Service

Activity 1: Matching
Terms

Match the term to the definition.

Definition		Term
1. _____	Clearness of communication	A. Conflict resolution
2. _____	Staying away from a person or issue instead of dealing with a conflict	B. Empathy
3. _____	Resolving conflict by both parties agreeing to something less or different than they originally wanted to achieve a peaceful resolution	C. Body language
4. _____	Process for settling a dispute or disagreement	D. Internal customer
5. _____	Nonverbal communication that includes posture, gestures, and facial expressions	E. Compromise
6. _____	Residents, families, and customers who are outside of the long term care facility	F. Service mentality
7. _____	Customers who are part of the same organization; supervisors and coworkers	G. Aggression
8. _____	Ability to understand and share the feelings or perspective of another person	H. Avoidance
9. _____	Hostile or violent behavior toward others	I. Clarity
10. _____	Dedication to making sure that customers' needs are satisfied	J. External customer

Activity 2: Word Scramble

Unscramble each term, and spell it correctly in the space provided.

Accommodation   Awareness   Body language
Communication   Compassion   Compromise
Conflict   Context   Customs
Dignity   Empathy   Eye contact
Listening   Reflection   Touch

1. TNIIYGD _____

2. MEPTHAY _____

3. USSCTOM _____

4. CMOIMNAOCUTNI _____

5. EILCTNREFO _____

6. ENLGITNIS _____

7. YEE OTTCCNA _____

8. CUHTO _____

9. YODB EGUAGNAL _____

10. ASRSEWNAE _____

11. LOINCTCF _____

12. TTOENXC _____

13. ROPMEOMICS _____

14. ASIMNOPSCO _____

15. MAOAOMNCDITCO _____

Activity 3: Word Search

```
H W F Q Q X E E Q O W K B C K J W X W O X J A H
T C O L L A B O R A T E Q R B I T B K Z Q R N R
C R F U F O G Y I B A V T U K L Z H C N Q Q V U
B L Y K N W P E I S P M I D D Q A T Z X Z V U D
V B N N Q L E C T S E M N T X E T N O C R G X C
Y U A N C X Y W W E Y B D K D U I H L X R U W V
X T R O T V M V K N E A F I T Y G O A E F C Y V
S B H I L U T J V E C B H C T D C E L Z L O A V
D C Y T I N G I D V O R W S F D K A E D V M D J
F N C N C L O V T I N Y S T O H T U L E F P Z T
A Y F E F D P N D S T G W D I X O V K B A M F
Z N H T D N F Q A N A Q X I O T H L E P E S J D
F K M T S X M N N E C B N N R S Z Y C K B S G G
S E W A A B C W M F T M S J B U N Y C Z F I V J
W F L W P E P D L E E H N N P R V O U E R O R E
F D Z I J O A J U D I A L H Z T N Z H S I N U T
Y Y R C M X O H A P H M W A A F T C L Q O E R E
L F P A H S F F S I J G H V L N B R K R J H P N
S S D V O P F E L U V R J I O N G C T S L Q X C
Z G O J Z D S Z S N L I C N I R X G F X G C Q F
X N I M M W O W I K B T U O Q O Q O E G K T R V
N Z R B B J N E T S I L D S I Q K F V R J J U B
E Y L P E J J G A N Z B E L P V H P I K Y X L J
B Y J T H X E R P M N G X W T G J U M S Z E L U
```

Context   Trust   Relationships
Smile   Conflict   Dignity
Attention   Collaborate   Compassion
Eye contact   Listen   Defensiveness

Activity 4: True or False
Conflict Resolution

Beside each statement, write T for TRUE or F for FALSE.

1. _____ Avoidance means trying to escape from, rather than deal with, an issue.

2. _____ Collaboration means that nobody wins the argument.

3. _____ Conflicts don't occur in long term care settings.

4. _____ Successfully resolving conflicts contributes to a positive work environment.

5. _____ You should never discuss personal issues in front of others, especially residents.

6. _____ Compromise means one person gives in to make the other happy.

7. _____ Always address the issue, not the person, to prevent him or her from becoming defensive.

8. _____ Use "you" statements instead of "I" statements so the other person does not feel attacked.

Activity 5: Multiple Choice

Circle the letter beside the correct answer.

1. A confused resident is behaving aggressively toward his roommate. As a nurse assistant, you should:
   A. Run down the hall to get the charge nurse.
   B. In a firm tone of voice, tell the resident to be quiet.
   C. Smile and talk in a friendly voice as you approach the resident.
   D. Approach the resident quickly and pull them into another room.

2. You are involved in a disagreement with a co-worker. In order to resolve the conflict, you should:
   A. Change the subject.
   B. Bluntly say what you feel.
   C. Avoid reacting defensively.
   D. Tell the co-worker they are wrong.

3. A new resident's family is very demanding, and you cannot seem to satisfy them. You should:
   A. Try to ignore their requests.
   B. Refer them to the charge nurse.
   C. Ask the resident to talk with them.
   D. Remember that work will be over soon.

4. If you want to be an effective listener for a resident in your care, you should NOT:
   A. Nod as they talk.
   B. Validate what they are saying.
   C. Maintain eye contact with them.
   D. Encourage them to tell their story quickly.

5. What is the BEST way to maximize a resident's capabilities?
   A. Always do exactly what the family wants you to do for their loved one.
   B. Allow the resident to do whatever they like.
   C. Work with the resident's capabilities and support them to their fullest.
   D. Make sure residents enjoy all aspects of their daily care routine.

Activity 6: Do's and Don'ts

In the space beside each example, write "Do" if it is an example of good communication and "Don't" if it is a bad example.

1. _____ Use a pleasant tone when you speak.

2. _____ Make eye contact when you speak and when you listen.

3. _____ Talk with food or gum in your mouth.

4. _____ Speak clearly and slowly.

5. _____ Use terms that the resident will understand.

6. _____ Reduce or eliminate other sounds such as radio or TV.

7. _____ Roll your eyes.

8. _____ Stop what you are doing to listen.

9. _____ Turn your back on the person you're talking with.

10. _____ Use medical terms or slang words.

11. _____ Give residents nicknames.

12. _____ Cover your mouth with your hand as you speak.

13. _____ Validate what the person is saying by nodding or agreeing.

14. _____ Clarify what's been said by repeating it in your own words.

15. _____ Fold your arms across your chest.

Activity 7: Fill in the Blank
Communication

Complete each sentence using the correct term.

Active	Communication	Conflict resolution
Defensiveness	Eye contact	Nonverbal
Open-ended questions	Verbal	

1. _____ communication involves spoken or written communication.

2. Body language, expressions, and touch are examples of _____ communication.

3. _____ listening includes observing body language and doing your best to understand the feelings behind the words.

4. Making _____ lets others know that you are interested and listening attentively.

5. Ask _____ to encourage residents to talk, rather than asking questions with yes or no answers.

6. _____ is the process of finding a peaceful solution to a disagreement.

7. _____ (reacting to a perceived threat), denial (ignoring or blocking true feelings or the truth about a situation), and feeling helpless or powerless in a situation are common barriers to communication.

8. Effective _____ is the key to creating trusting relationships with the people you care for and work with.

Activity 8: Question and Answer

1. What are five ways to promote effective communication?

    _____

    _____

    _____

    _____

    _____

2. What are two specific techniques that can improve communication with residents who have these impairments?

    A. Visual impairment

    _____

    _____

    B. Hearing loss

    _____

    _____

    C. Depression or withdrawal

    _____

    _____

    D. Speech impairment

    _____

    _____

    E. Memory loss

    _____

    _____

3. Describe a situation in which someone's nonverbal message did not match their verbal message.

    _____

    _____

    _____

Maintaining Quality of Life
Activity 1: Fill in the Blank

Complete each sentence using the correct term.

Autonomy   History

Family   Respect

Food   Self-esteem

Hierarchy of needs   Status

1. Maslow's _____ includes physical, security, social, status, and self-fulfillment needs.

2. Physical needs are those that are essential to human life such as oxygen, _____, and water.

3. _____ is a sense of valuing oneself and the skills and talents that make you unique.

4. A resident's personal _____ impacts quality of life.

5. If a resident receives respect and recognition from others, they have _____.

6. _____ means making decisions for oneself and being independent.

7. You will often have more contact with residents than their own _____ members do.

8. Residents must be treated with _____ and kindness at all times.

AHCA
AMERICAN HEALTH CARE ASSOCIATION

Activity 2: True or False

Beside each statement, write T for TRUE or F for FALSE.

1. _____ A resident who doesn't attend religious services does not have spiritual needs.

2. _____ A resident has less independence if you do everything for them.

3. _____ As a resident becomes more dependent on staff, they may have less self-worth.

4. _____ A frail or confused resident doesn't have sexual needs.

5. _____ A person's status needs must be met before they can meet their social needs.

6. _____ If a resident is in pain, their social needs become less important.

7. _____ Physical needs must be met before status needs can take priority.

8. _____ Knowing a resident well is the best way for you to meet their needs.

9. _____ Once a person has met a higher level need, they never have to worry about meeting a lower level need.

10. _____ How we feel about ourselves can depend on how others react to us.

Activity 3: Word Search

Themes of Care

```
Z  F  P  J  X  M  U  L  Q  B  I  H  Z  D  G  O  B  H  T  K  Y  J  W  Y
W  E  Y  D  Y  Z  P  R  Y  L  N  S  O  U  R  S  Y  W  K  W  G  Y  R  T
A  N  K  I  O  Q  C  R  O  P  F  E  F  J  R  C  I  M  F  S  U  F  Y  W
Y  T  B  G  O  G  Q  C  D  L  E  I  T  J  B  D  N  D  Y  Z  T  C  D  M
F  V  H  N  B  Z  J  Q  R  N  C  T  E  M  E  H  T  V  J  T  I  E  J  O
I  X  Y  I  S  E  G  N  H  R  T  I  G  V  Q  D  D  J  S  N  M  P  J  G
P  B  J  T  E  B  C  O  G  B  I  L  S  V  D  W  A  G  R  O  E  L  K  G
W  A  F  Y  R  W  Z  I  T  Q  O  I  D  E  F  P  E  G  C  E  M  B  A  V
O  E  C  T  V  U  D  T  X  J  N  B  I  G  N  I  Q  S  I  Z  A  L  C  H
G  V  H  E  A  J  R  A  P  B  C  A  B  W  P  X  H  V  X  H  N  S  U  U
B  A  M  F  T  V  Q  C  H  I  O  P  H  X  U  S  E  C  D  S  A  N  F  W
L  K  G  A  I  M  G  I  V  Y  N  A  S  Y  K  J  E  F  F  O  G  B  U  J
A  Q  E  S  O  V  W  N  R  X  T  C  E  L  Y  I  K  D  S  O  E  O  E  A
Z  Y  Y  C  N  E  O  U  U  R  R  G  E  S  E  V  G  H  B  D  M  Z  R  D
U  C  Y  F  J  V  K  M  L  U  O  N  Y  M  O  N  O  T  U  A  E  K  A  Z
U  R  L  Y  O  U  C  M  J  V  L  I  I  J  G  J  A  Z  N  N  N  I  C  G
G  G  L  X  O  F  R  O  Y  K  U  Z  L  P  J  H  R  B  D  N  T  S  L  K
Y  O  D  I  W  J  V  C  V  U  N  I  G  O  M  J  L  Z  R  S  O  W  K  E
R  R  J  T  P  K  P  S  V  Z  I  M  C  W  I  C  Q  T  B  X  H  L  X  Y
E  Z  J  Z  S  O  V  O  K  W  Z  I  T  C  E  P  S  E  R  P  T  H  Y  K
P  A  C  W  U  K  V  N  S  G  J  X  S  H  E  G  O  P  U  T  E  G  M  I
O  Q  I  D  M  K  X  F  P  R  P  A  B  P  L  O  X  F  A  Q  B  K  L  E
N  I  R  V  G  U  G  T  C  U  Y  M  N  S  N  V  J  S  W  G  A  T  B  N
R  I  G  M  Z  R  L  W  R  S  X  I  N  O  I  S  S  I  M  R  E  P  I  J
```

Care	Permission	Dignity
Theme	Time management	Maximizing capabilities
Observation	Safety	Autonomy
Infection control	Respect	Communication

Activity 4: Yes or No

Beside each statement, write YES if the resident's dignity is promoted, or NO if the resident's dignity is not promoted.

1. _____ Ask permission before giving care to the resident.

2. _____ Call the resident by their preferred name.

3. _____ Insist that the resident wear an outfit you've chosen.

4. _____ Be considerate of the resident's needs, wants, and rights.

5. _____ Rush the resident through their morning care.

6. _____ Take the resident to an activity they won't understand.

7. _____ Treat the resident like a customer.

8. _____ Respect the resident's values, culture, and religion.

9. _____ Leave the door open while the resident gets dressed.

10. _____ Take an interest in the resident's stories.

11. _____ Use baby talk when speaking to the resident.

12. _____ Offer the resident choices.

13. _____ Ask for permission to enter the resident's room.

14. _____ Answer the resident's call light promptly.

15. _____ Touch the resident's belongings without permission.

Activity 5: Multiple Choice

Circle the letter beside the correct answer.

1. Your perception of a resident can be affected by:
   A. Their favorite color.
   B. A hot and humid day.
   C. Your own values and culture.
   D. The resident's clothing choices.

2. What is the BEST way to support a resident's quality of life?
   A. Style their hair in a new way.
   B. Knock on their door as you open it.
   C. Treat them with dignity and respect.
   D. Be friendly whenever their family visits.

3. The goal of activities is to:
   A. Keep the activities director employed.
   B. Help residents become actively engaged.
   C. Make decorations for all national holidays.
   D. Give nurse assistants a few minutes of free time.

4. The goal of an Eden alternative nursing facility is to:
   A. Plant flower and vegetable gardens.
   B. Allow residents to care for plants and pets.
   C. Eliminate loneliness, helplessness, and boredom.
   D. Operate daycare centers and after-school programs.

5. What is the most important part of a nurse assistant's job?
   A. Getting everything done.
   B. Meeting all the resident's needs.
   C. Helping the resident get dressed.
   D. Seeing that residents get fed on time.

Activity 6: Questions to Consider

Why is dignity important to residents?

_____

_____

_____

_____

Describe a situation in which you were not treated with dignity. How did you feel?

_____

_____

_____

_____

_____

What do you think happens to residents when they are not treated with dignity?

_____

_____

_____

_____

_____

If a resident is unhappy with some aspect of their care, what can they expect from you?

_____

_____

_____

_____

_____

Activity 7: Question and Answer

Read each question. Choose the key term that answers the question, and write that term on the line provided.

Family   Feedback   Stress   Guilt

1. When someone has committed an offense or believes they have done something wrong to another person, what emotion might they feel?

   _____

2. What is the term for people who are important to a resident, or related to the resident by marriage or ancestry?

   _____

3. When someone has a physical or emotional reaction to an event or situation, and that reaction causes them mental tension, what is the reaction called?

   _____

4. When we receive information that is corrective or evaluative, what is that information called?

   _____

Activity 8: What Would You Say?

Read the following situations and circle the best response to the following questions.

1. Mrs. Chesnutt, a resident in your care, has emphysema and her health is failing. Her daughter has been critical of her mother's care during her last two visits. She believes staff could be doing more to help her mother improve. What should you say to her?

   A. "I give your mother the best care I can."

   B. "You need to accept the fact that your mother isn't going to get better."

   C. "I can see that you're worried, and I'm sorry you have concerns. Would you like for me to get the charge nurse?"

2. Mr. Lomax is a new resident. He is angry that his family has put him in a nursing facility. When his family members come to visit, he barely speaks to them. What can you say to make the family feel better?

   A. "Mr. Lomax will adjust before you know it."

   B. "This is just a phase. Why don't you put off your next visit until he's had time to adjust?"

   C. "Mr. Lomax is getting the very best care. Is there anything we can do to make your visits more pleasant?"

3. Mrs. White's daughter likes to bring her mother home-cooked foods. But recently the doctor prescribed a low-salt diet, which would mean an end to her meals of collard greens and green beans with bacon. If Mrs. White and her daughter refuse to cooperate, what should you do?

   A. Don't say anything.

   B. Report the situation to the charge nurse.

   C. Remind them about the doctor's orders, but don't insist on their cooperation.

4. Mrs. Cadden's daughter wants to help transfer her mother from the bed to a wheelchair. She insists that the way they did it at home is safer for her mother than the method staff uses. What should you say?

   A. "There is no way I can allow you to do that."

   B. "Let me get the charge nurse so she can review the transfer."

   C. "Go ahead and move her, but the facility isn't responsible if she falls."

5. Mrs. Hearn has just returned to the facility from the hospital. She is weak and must be in a wheelchair because of her brief illness. The doctor's orders are for staff to begin ambulating her three times a day using a walker. Her son is visiting and tells you it is too soon for his mother to be walking. What should you say?

   A. "I'm sorry, Mr. Hearn, but I've got orders to walk your mother. It's my job and I'm going to do it."

   B. "I know you're concerned, but your mother will continue to lose strength if she doesn't start walking."

   C. "I know I'm right about this, Mr. Hearn. I think you should step out of the room."

Resident Rights
Activity 1: Multiple Choice

Circle the letter beside the correct answer.

1. Residents of nursing facilities have the same rights as:
   A. All children.
   B. All U.S. citizens.
   C. All human beings.
   D. All doctors.

2. Mrs. Ludlow asks to see her financial records and have them explained to her. She is exercising her right to:
   A. Privacy.
   B. Information.
   C. Confidentiality.
   D. Self-determination.

3. A resident must be told that they are to be discharged or transferred:
   A. As soon as staff is told.
   B. One day before the move.
   C. At least 30 days in advance.
   D. At least two hours in advance.

4. Screening of potential nurse assistants may include:
   A. Inspection of their wardrobe.
   B. Checks of family members.
   C. Home safety inspection.
   D. Criminal background checks.

5. Mr. Chang returns to his room and discovers he has a new roommate. Which of his rights has been violated?
   A. Right to information.
   B. Right to exercise one's rights.
   C. Right to notification of change.
   D. Right to privacy and confidentiality.

Activity 2: Identify the Right

For each example, select the resident right that is involved. Write it in on the line below the example.

Right to privacy	Rights to information
Rights to choose	Right to exercise your rights
Protection of residents' personal funds	Grievance rights
Transfer and discharge rights	Right to be free from restraint and abuse

1. You notice that a resident is giving out small amounts of cash to other residents.

   _____

2. The resident is uneasy and tries to stay covered up while taking a bath.

   _____

3. The resident is about to be transferred to another wing of the facility.

   _____

4. A resident's daughter wants to see his medical record and care plan.

   _____

5. A staff member loses their temper and grabs a resident's arm.

   _____

6. A resident's family wants to put their complaints in writing.

   _____

7. A resident doesn't like the way a medication makes them feel; they refuse to take it.

   _____

8. A resident wants to maintain contact with friends from her church.

   _____

Activity 3: Matching
Examples of Abuse

Read the examples of abuse. Place the letter of the correct term for that form of abuse next to the example.

Example

1. _____ A resident is shaken by an angry nurse assistant.
2. _____ A bed-ridden resident is not turned as often as they should be.
3. _____ A resident is sedated so they won't wander.
4. _____ Making fun of a resident.
5. _____ Punishing a resident by slapping them.
6. _____ Locking a resident in a room against their will.
7. _____ Allowing one resident to touch another in a sexual way.
8. _____ Stealing a resident's money.
9. _____ Using a device that forces a resident to remain seated.
10. _____ Making a threatening remark to a resident.
11. _____ Failing to do what another nurse assistant would do in the same situation.

Term

A. Theft

B. Neglect

C. Physical abuse

D. Corporal punishment

E. Involuntary seclusion

F. Mental abuse

G. Negligence

H. Verbal abuse

I. Chemical restraint

J. Sexual abuse

K. Physical restraint

Activity 4: Matching

Match the term to the definition.

Term | Definition

1. _____ Advocate

A. Someone in need of special care, support, or protection because of age, disability, or risk of abuse or neglect

2. _____ Allegation

B. A person's statement or intended legal action

3. _____ Ombudsman

C. Someone who takes the side of another person and speaks for them

4. _____ Confidentiality

D. Freedom to make your own choices and choose your own actions

5. _____ Vulnerable adult

E. Keeping information private

6. _____ Incident

F. Of the act of getting revenge or punishing a person for doing something

7. _____ Neglect

G. Failure to do something that should have been done

8. _____ Retaliation

H. Someone charged with investigating complaints by residents or others about violations of rights

9. _____ Right

I. Move to another room in the facility

10. _____ Securing

J. A person's state or situation

11. _____ Self-determination

K. Something one has a just or legal claim to

12. _____ Sentimental value

L. Something happens that is unusual

13. _____ Status

M. Making something safe

14. _____ Transfer

N. An object of value because of associations and memories it has for the owner

Activity 5: Word Search

```
W  B  S  R  B  Y  N  M  M  Z  P  G  I  F  T  H  K  N  U  E  G  H  H  U
R  I  I  R  E  F  S  N  A  R  T  J  Q  E  C  I  H  F  Z  O  V  I  Q  S
A  G  I  L  N  I  E  H  U  V  W  T  S  G  K  F  P  N  J  A  A  T  P  X
K  S  R  E  P  O  R  T  I  N  G  C  T  J  E  J  U  X  R  T  C  I  B  Z
W  A  Z  W  Z  F  T  R  F  R  C  A  H  L  V  C  C  N  Q  N  K  F  T  C
X  J  B  M  E  R  C  E  R  P  F  E  G  F  Q  U  N  Y  G  L  E  Z  H  O
D  A  Y  L  R  Y  N  Y  I  S  Y  C  I  C  T  X  H  A  H  S  Z  E  P  I
O  J  N  J  N  X  X  E  G  P  K  I  R  U  O  D  H  G  V  G  T  X  T  M
M  S  X  V  P  K  U  R  H  G  J  T  N  J  A  L  K  Y  K  E  T  O  Y  F
E  U  R  Q  G  E  F  X  T  J  R  S  M  R  I  E  S  U  B  A  I  U  L  W
S  D  Q  W  S  L  U  E  T  R  L  U  Q  B  X  A  W  L  C  L  F  R  Q  E
T  O  F  P  O  A  D  H  O  O  H  J  U  P  K  O  A  B  I  A  G  K  G  I
I  M  R  L  Q  S  B  J  C  A  G  R  U  P  Y  L  T  G  N  O  D  J  X  V
C  B  G  R  Z  U  O  Q  H  R  U  E  I  G  I  Q  V  T  L  G  Y  F  P  T
V  U  H  C  M  M  N  K  O  K  L  D  R  E  S  T  R  A  I  N  T  S  F  H
I  D  T  X  R  T  F  F  O  D  X  L  I  F  I  N  A  L  R  E  P  O  R  G
O  S  Z  A  W  S  L  E  S  Q  Z  E  G  L  N  E  G  L  E  C  T  V  W  I
L  M  H  P  C  A  H  T  E  Q  O  X  H  S  N  C  E  K  M  D  O  J  F  R
E  A  C  N  N  F  Q  L  T  S  K  R  X  B  Y  X  H  B  B  G  R  C  V  F
N  N  B  W  E  Q  I  I  D  U  C  C  O  B  S  E  R  V  A  T  I  O  N  T
C  E  E  P  T  Y  E  C  A  U  N  I  P  B  P  H  M  H  L  V  R  I  W  B
E  B  M  K  O  U  K  S  J  A  T  S  X  G  O  S  F  R  N  Z  O  N  A  I
T  M  K  W  E  E  T  A  N  F  N  V  Y  O  F  Y  I  I  J  Z  M  W  O  G
W  G  H  F  M  I  S  T  R  E  A  T  M  E  N  T  D  S  T  W  V  T  N  V
```

Neglect	Grievance	Elder Justice Act
Restraint	Rights	Harm
Abuse	Ombudsman	Transfer
Right	Right to choose	Observation
Reporting	Domestic violence	Mistreatment

Preventing Infections While Providing Personal Care

CHAPTER 5

Activity 1: Matching

Match the term to the definition.

Definition

1. _____ Measures taken to prevent the airborne transmission of pathogens

2. _____ Measures taken to prevent the spread of infection caused by microorganisms transmitted by direct or indirect contact

3. _____ Measures taken to prevent the spread of infection caused by microorganisms transmitted by droplets produced by coughing, sneezing, talking, or performing procedures

4. _____ Infected oral or nasal secretions transmitted via the eyes, nose, or mouth of another person

5. _____ Infection spread by microorganisms contained in particles or droplets suspended in air

6. _____ The opening by which a microorganism enters the host

7. _____ Route taken by microorganisms leaving the body

8. _____ Evidence-based practices designed to prevent transmission of infectious disease

9. _____ Means by which a microorganism is transferred from one carrier to another

10. _____ Measures taken to prevent the spread of infection from an infected resident to other people

Term

A. Portal of exit

B. Standard precautions

C. Portal of entry

D. Isolation precautions

E. Airborne precautions

F. Mode of transmission

G. Airborne transmission

H. Droplet spread

I. Droplet precautions

J. Contact precautions

Activity 2: Crossword

Terms

Antibiotic

Bacteria

Chain of infection

Disinfection

Exposure

Fungus

Immunization

Infection

Microorganisms

Nonpathogenic

Outbreak

Standard precautions

Virus

Across

1 Organisms that cannot be seen with the naked eye; some capable of causing infection

3 Type of microorganism that can cause infection; examples are yeast and mold

9 Evidence-based practices designed to prevent transmission of infectious disease

11 Administration of a vaccine to prevent a specific infectious disease

12 Describes microorganisms that do not cause infection

13 Process that kills or inhibits the growth of virtually all microorganisms on objects and surfaces

Down

2 Sudden increase in cases of a disease within a certain geographic area

4 Process by which infection is spread

5 Single-celled microorganisms that may cause infection

6 Invasion and multiplication of microorganisms such as bacteria and viruses that are not normally present in the body

7 Being in the vicinity of or in contact with an infectious microorganism

8 Name of a drug that inhibits the growth of or kills certain microorganisms.

10 A type of microorganism that survives only in living things

Activity 3: Multiple Choice

Circle the letter beside the correct answer.

1. Bacteria is a type of:
   A. Fungi
   B. Influenza
   C. Antibiotic
   D. Microorganism

2. A microorganism that cannot cause infection is:
   A. Bacteria
   B. Antibiotic
   C. Pathogenic
   D. Nonpathogenic

3. Mrs. Reynolds had surgery recently and is at risk of getting an infection. In the chain of infection, what is she called?
   A. Reservoir
   B. Portal of exit
   C. Portal of entry
   D. Susceptible host

4. Direct transmission of a microorganism occurs by:
   A. Handling soiled linens
   B. Using a contaminated phone
   C. Kissing or sexual intercourse
   D. Eating off someone else's plate

Activity 4: True or False

Beside the statement, write T for TRUE or F for FALSE.

1. _____ The most important way to prevent the spread of infection is by washing your hands.

2. _____ It is important to rinse your hands from your fingertips down to your wrists after you've washed them with soap.

3. _____ Diarrhea is frequent liquid stools.

4. _____ Protection is not required when assisting a resident with toileting.

5. _____ Single-use gloves can be reused if they don't look dirty.

6. _____ A disinfectant should be used to clean up blood or other bodily fluids.

7. _____ You don't need to wash your hands after a procedure if you were wearing gloves.

8. _____ If a resident is on isolation precautions, only a nurse can provide their care.

9. _____ All objects that have been used by a resident or caregiver are considered dirty.

10. _____ Residents who are on isolation precautions may need emotional support from staff and family.

Activity 5: Matching

Match the term to the definition.

Term		Definition
1. _____ Airborne transmission		A. Written information sheets describing chemicals used in a facility
2. _____ Barrier		B. Openings in the body where microorganisms can enter
3. _____ Chicken pox		C. Transmission of infection by an intermediate object, such as food, water, medical equipment, or a person's hands, to the portal of entry of a susceptible host
4. _____ Direct transmission		D. Something that impedes or separates a person from an infectious microorganism
5. _____ SDS		E. Direct transfer of microorganisms from one person to another
6. _____ Indirect transmission		F. A person, animal, or environment in which an infectious agent lives
7. _____ Intestines		G. Transfer an infectious agent from one person or place to another
8. _____ Outbreak		H. Route of transmission occurs when the reservoir coughs microorganisms into the air and a susceptible host breathes them into the lungs
9. _____ Portal of entry		I. Part of the digestive tract through which food passes after leaving the stomach; helps digest food and eliminate waste
10. _____ Reservoir		J. Microorganisms that are always present, that usually do not cause disease
11. _____ Natural flora		K. Dramatic, sudden increase in cases of a particular disease or harmful organisms
12. _____ Transmit		L. Contagious disease caused by a virus; one symptom is a low-grade fever

Activity 6: Spell It Out

Using the word list below and the definition provided in each example, complete the spelling of the term.

Antibiotics   Bacteria   Diarrhea   Fungi

Gonorrhea   Human immunodeficiency virus   Immunization   Infection

Measles   Microorganism   Nonpathogenic   Pathogenic

Syphilis   Tuberculosis   Virus

1. A kind of microorganism like yeast and mold. ____ ____ ____GI

2. Microorganisms or substances that can produce disease. ____ ____ TH ____ G____ ____I____

3. Infectious, bacterial, communicable disease primarily affecting the lungs, also known as TB.

   T ____ B____ ____C____ ____ ____S____ ____

4. Contagious bacterial venereal infection that is sexually transmitted.

   G____ N____ R____ ____E____

5. Condition produced when an infective agent becomes established in or on a suitable host.

   ____ ____F____ ____ ____ ____ ____N

6. Drugs that reduce or kill microorganisms. ____N____ ____B____ ____ T____ ____ ____

7. One-celled microorganisms that may cause infection. B____ ____T____R____ ____

8. Contagious disease cause by a virus that produces red spots on the skin. M____ ____S____ ____S

9. Microorganisms that do not cause infection. N____ ____P____ ____ ____ ____G____ ____ ____ ____ C

10. Viral infection transmitted by contact with blood and other body fluids such as semen and vaginal secretions, also known as HIV.

    ____ ____M____N

    I____ M____ ____ ____D____ ____ ____ ____ ____ ____N____ ____

    V____ R____ ____

11. A type of microorganism that survives only in living things. ____ ____R____S

12. Virus, bacteria, or fungus that cannot be seen with the naked eye; also called a germ.

    ____ ____C____ ____ ____RG____ ____ ____ ____M

13. A chronic contagious venereal infection that is sexually transmitted.

    ____Y____ ____ ____L____ ____

14. Administration of a vaccine to make the person immune (not susceptible) to a specific infection.

    ____ ____M____ ____ ____Z____T____ ____ ____

15. Condition indicated by frequent and liquid stools. ____I____R____ ____ ____A

Activity 7: Fill in the Blank

Complete each sentence using the correct term.

Biohazard	Condom	Contaminated
Emesis	Invasive	Isolation precautions
Sanitation	Secretions	Sterilization

1. If something is impure or unclean, it is _____.

2. _____ is the term for something that enters the body.

3. _____ is the promotion of hygiene and prevention of disease by maintaining clean conditions.

4. A(n) _____ is a thin, flexible sheath commonly made of latex rubber, worn over the penis to reduce the risk of pregnancy and transmission of sexually transmitted diseases.

5. _____ _____ are measures taken to prevent the spread of infection from an infected resident to other people.

6. _____ causes the complete elimination or destruction of all microbial life.

7. A(n) _____ is anything that is harmful or potentially harmful to humans or the environment.

8. Substances like saliva, mucus, perspiration, tears, etc. are called _____.

9. A(n) _____ basin is used for collecting body fluids during procedures or for vomiting.

Activity 8: Multiple Choice

Personal Care

Circle the letter beside the correct answer.

1. As you provide personal care, you should:
   A. Change your uniform.
   B. Always wear a gown, gloves, and mask.
   C. Protect the resident's dignity and privacy.
   D. Ask the resident's roommate to stay in the room.

2. Why is it important to wear gloves when you provide mouth care?
   A. In case the resident's gums bleed.
   B. The resident may have bad breath.
   C. So you won't have to wash your hands.
   D. In case you get toothpaste on your hands.

3. When is the bath water changed during a bed bath?
   A. Before washing the perineum.
   B. After washing the face and neck.
   C. After washing the feet and hands.
   D. Any time the water gets cold, soapy, or dirty.

4. What is the correct way to wash the female perineal area?
   A. Wash the anus first, then the labia.
   B. Wash the pubic area first, then the anus.
   C. Wash the entire area in a circular motion.
   D. Wash back and forth over the entire area twice.

5. When you are helping to dress a resident with a paralyzed arm you should:
   A. Put the shirt on the weak arm last.
   B. Put the shirt on the weak arm first.
   C. Put the shirt on the arm closest to you.
   D. Put the shirt on the arm farthest from you.

Activity 9: Situation and Response

In the space provided by each situation, write the letter of the correct response.

Situation

1. _____ Mrs. Bertram, a blind resident in your care, is going out to lunch with her daughter. She wants to look her best for the outing.

2. _____ You find a red spot on a resident's hip. It doesn't go away.

3. _____ Mrs. Crawford has limited mobility in her left shoulder and needs help getting ready for bed.

4. _____ Mr. Price has a chronic problem with dizziness.

5. _____ Mrs. Rushworth insists on wearing a yellow and orange floral blouse with red and black plaid pants.

Response

A. Help the resident by unzipping their dress. As you put a gown on the resident, put the sleeve on their left arm first.

B. Suggest the resident sit at the side of the bed as you help them dress. Help the resident to put on and take off their shoes and socks.

C. Help the resident choose color-coordinated clothes. Get the clothes out of the closet and help the resident put them on.

D. Allow the resident to choose what they want to wear.

E. Let the charge nurse know about the change in the resident's condition immediately.

Activity 10: Chain of Infection

In the diagram below, write the six steps/conditions in the chain of infection in the order by which infection occurs.

Microorganism   Portal of entry   Portal of exit
Reservoir   Susceptible host   Transmission

6th _____   _____ 1st

5th _____   _____ 2nd

4th _____   _____ 3rd

Safety and Emergency Care
Activity 1: Word Search
Dangers and Precautions

```
I  N  M  J  E  J  S  Z  L  H  W  M  D  O  G  Y  Y  Y  C  G  J  Y  O  S
M  X  O  P  Y  Y  P  Q  A  N  F  C  U  V  G  M  C  P  L  R  G  X  S  N
I  W  S  D  G  P  E  X  S  S  F  A  A  S  P  P  T  O  M  E  J  U  M  E
K  M  S  H  W  E  G  B  H  T  Z  C  L  W  Y  U  V  L  C  G  K  W  Y  G
C  Z  Z  V  C  L  B  G  C  X  C  Y  G  L  F  E  A  K  L  C  K  D  A  O
N  L  O  F  W  M  B  Q  X  I  P  U  L  S  V  X  H  P  D  C  S  H  H
O  V  K  T  X  Z  W  P  N  F  T  P  U  C  S  W  W  L  M  E  I  P  S  T
I  S  K  P  Z  P  K  A  I  J  S  I  U  W  H  G  O  W  N  H  T  B  O  A
T  N  Q  W  O  P  T  R  Z  B  D  B  W  B  X  O  V  I  T  V  S  S  N  P
A  R  H  N  O  I  S  N  D  S  H  Y  G  T  K  F  K  D  N  C  E  A  U  E
U  H  X  J  O  T  J  F  V  P  G  O  G  G  L  E  S  I  P  E  L  F  R  N
C  Q  B  N  A  C  F  U  Z  T  T  D  E  G  O  V  Y  N  N  Q  D  V  F  R
A  J  X  I  A  J  Q  K  U  D  I  S  A  S  T  E  R  S  J  G  E  D  B  O
V  M  D  N  O  P  R  E  P  A  R  A  T  I  O  N  M  C  K  Y  E  F  H  B
E  R  C  Z  S  S  I  T  I  T  A  P  E  H  U  V  B  X  D  A  N  C  H  D
Z  X  S  C  I  N  A  H  C  E  M  Y  D  O  B  U  P  H  K  Z  L  K  V  O
Q  S  N  O  I  T  U  A  C  E  R  P  D  R  A  D  N  A  T  S  C  B  D  O
O  O  V  T  L  E  B  R  E  F  S  N  A  R  T  Z  S  D  P  P  P  B  O  L
F  R  S  K  T  L  T  W  Q  B  F  I  Z  F  Y  G  E  J  W  T  J  K  F  B
U  V  V  L  F  U  J  M  J  K  U  R  X  J  Q  A  I  Y  O  F  V  L  F  G
Q  A  N  M  C  U  X  E  B  B  S  Y  L  P  U  W  Z  X  R  G  O  K  L  O
B  D  H  J  O  P  N  M  J  T  X  A  U  B  Y  S  U  M  M  R  K  P  B  U
U  F  N  B  W  L  Y  S  C  B  W  V  M  S  C  D  R  N  X  K  Y  V  T  W
H  A  N  D  W  A  S  H  I  N  G  W  U  H  K  V  E  N  W  R  H  X  J  R
```

First aid	Transfer belt	Bloodborne pathogens	Mask
Seizure	Body mechanics	OSHA	Goggles
Choking	Preparation	Standard precautions	Gloves
Evacuation	Vaccination	Needlestick	
Disasters	Fluids	Handwashing	
Falls	Hepatitis	Gown	

Activity 2: Matching

Match the term to the correct definition.

Term

1. _____ Biceps

2. _____ Body mechanics

3. _____ Ergonomics

4. _____ External evacuation

5. _____ Internal evacuation

6. _____ Hepatitis

7. _____ Exposure

8. _____ Standard precautions

9. _____ Disinfectant

10. _____ Gait belt

Definition

A. Used to help steady a resident during transfers or walking

B. Infection of the liver

C. Condition of being in direct or indirect contact with an infectious microorganism

D. Moving residents to another section within the facility for safety

E. Principles of using your body efficiently to do something

F. Study of relationships between workers' physical capabilities and their job tasks

G. An agent that inactivates microorganisms on inanimate objects

H. Recommendations from CDC for facilities to use in handling blood, body fluids, secretions, excretion (except sweat), non-intact skin, such as cuts and wounds, and mucous membranes of all residents to prevent infection

I. Moving residents out of the facility to another site for safety

J. Strong arm muscles used for lifting

Activity 3: Multiple Choice

Circle the letter beside the correct answer.

1. What is the FIRST step in the five-step approach to preventing injuries when caring for a resident?
   A. Follow the care plan.
   B. Determine the resident's capabilities.
   C. Determine the equipment you will need.
   D. Evaluate the success of the tasks you have performed.

2. Pivot discs are used to help a resident:
   A. Exercise.
   B. Use a walker.
   C. Transfer from the bed to chair.
   D. Perform range-of-motion exercises.

3. If you enter a room where there is a fire, what should you do FIRST?
   A. Stop and quickly assess the situation.
   B. Immediately remove all residents from the area.
   C. When everyone is out, close the door to the room.
   D. Yell for help and sound an alarm if one is present.

4. What is the hug position?
   A. A policy having to do with affection between residents.
   B. Holding an object or person close to you as you move them.
   C. Two nurse assistants hug the resident from either side as they lift.
   D. A means of limiting inappropriate behaviors between staff and residents.

5. A resident's bed should be kept in its lowest position when:
   A. You are changing the sheets.
   B. You are giving the resident a bed bath.
   C. The resident is resting in the bed or the bed is empty.
   D. Family is coming to visit and there aren't enough chairs.

6. The goal of standard precautions is to:
   A. Prevent residents and staff from slipping or falling down.
   B. Prevent residents from wandering away from the facility.
   C. Prevent the airborne transmission of the cold and flu viruses.
   D. Prevent the transmission of diseases when handling bodily fluids.

Activity 4: Safe and Unsafe

Read each example. In the blank provided, write an S if the example is a SAFE practice or a U if it is an UNSAFE practice.

1. _____ Wait for housekeeping to clean up a small spill in the hallway.

2. _____ Consider your own strength and body mechanics before you move a resident.

3. _____ Respond to a resident's call light when you have the time.

4. _____ Wear nonskid shoes.

5. _____ Turn the hallway lights off at night.

6. _____ Leave the resident's slippers by their bed in case they get up in the night.

7. _____ Consider the resident's capabilities before you transfer them.

8. _____ Bend your knees and lift using your leg and arm muscles, not your back.

9. _____ Get a good grip on the resident by holding on to their shirt collar.

10. _____ Eliminate clutter in the resident's room and bathroom.

11. _____ Set up a new resident's radio using an extension cord.

12. _____ If a resident gets a chemical on their skin, rinse it off with lots of running water and notify the nurse immediately.

13. _____ Lean an empty oxygen tank against the wall, outside a resident's room.

14. _____ Handle bottles of hazardous chemicals when you don't know their contents.

Activity 5: Should and Should Not

Read each example. In the blank provided, write an S if the example is a step you SHOULD take or a SN if it is step you SHOULD NOT take in the event of a fire.

1. _____ Attempt to put out a fire that is climbing up a wall.

2. _____ Attempt to put out a small fire in a trash can.

3. _____ Open the windows in a room where there's a fire.

4. _____ Use oxygen to put out a fire.

5. _____ Remove residents from a room where there is a fire and close the door.

6. _____ Yell for help, and sound an alarm if present.

7. _____ Open a door when you see smoke coming from underneath it.

8. _____ Evacuate residents at immediate risk to the end of the farthest wing from the fire.

9. _____ Throw water on a large fire.

10. _____ Close the door to a room that's on fire.

Activity 6: Matching
Safety Documentation

Match each example of safety documentation to the correct term.

Term

1. _____ Access to Employee Exposure and Medical Records Standard

2. _____ Safety Data Sheet (SDS)

3. _____ Incident report

Example

A. A report on an accident involving staff or residents.

B. A sheet that lists a substance's chemical contents, fire and health hazards, use precautions, cleanup procedures, disposal requirements, needed personal protective equipment, and first aid procedures.

C. An OSHA publication explaining your right to see your medical records, a chemical inventory list, and safety data sheets.

Activity 7: Multiple Choice
Emergency Care

Circle the letter beside the correct answer.

1. In any emergency, a nurse assistant should stay with the resident, call for help, and:
   A. Remain calm.
   B. Always give first aid.
   C. Always give CPR.
   D. Take the resident's pulse.

2. You discover that a resident has a deep cut on their arm. What is the FIRST step you take?
   A. Put pressure on the wound.
   B. Call for the nurse.
   C. Have the resident lie down.
   D. Clean up any spilled blood.

3. Heart attacks are caused by:
   A. Difficulty breathing.
   B. Weakness and fatigue.
   C. A rapid, weak, irregular pulse.
   D. A blockage in the coronary arteries.

4. Cardiopulmonary resuscitation (CPR) is performed on a resident who:
   A. Is choking.
   B. Is in cardiac arrest.
   C. Has cold and clammy skin.
   D. Does not respond to your touch.

5. What is one immediate treatment the charge nurse may ask you to do for a burn?
   A. Put butter or margarine on the burn.
   B. Run cold water over the burn.
   C. Put soap on the burn.
   D. Remove any jewelry that has stuck to the skin.

Activity 8: True or False

Beside each statement, write T for TRUE or F for FALSE.

1. _____ CPR should be performed on any unconscious resident.

2. _____ Chest pain is a symptom of a seizure.

3. _____ A person is hemorrhaging if they have lost 3 quarts of blood.

4. _____ Unusual thirst can be a symptom of shock.

5. _____ The Heimlich maneuver is done to assist a person in cardiac arrest.

6. _____ Shock occurs when the body's organs are receiving too much oxygen.

7. _____ Residents and visitors always know not to smoke in a room where oxygen is in use.

8. _____ Heart attacks are caused by palpitations.

9. _____ It is natural to feel nervous and scared during an emergency.

10. _____ Cardiac arrest can result from a heart attack.

11. _____ An airway obstruction causes a person to stop breathing.

12. _____ Before having a seizure, a resident may feel an aura.

13. _____ Electrical burns are caused by direct exposure to fire.

14. _____ It's important to manage your own feelings in an emergency.

15. _____ F. A. S. T. represents the symptoms signs of a stroke.

Activity 9: Crossword

Terms to Know

Antibody	Aura	Cardiac arrest	Cardiopulmonary resuscitation
Cholesterol	Ergonomics	Hemorrhage	Hepatitis
Myocardial infarction	Plaque	Seizure	Shock

Across

4 Commonly called a heart attack

6 Fatty deposit on blood vessel walls

7 Excessive or uncontrolled bleeding

8 Complete cessation of heart activity (no heartbeat)

11 Viral infection of the liver

12 Emergency procedure to restore cardiopulmonary function

Down

1 Medical emergency in which body tissues and organs are not receiving adequate blood and oxygen

2 Study of the interaction of workers and their environment; its principles drive the design of equipment and work environments

3 Abnormal electrical activity in the brain that causes sudden, involuntary muscle movements

5 Fatty substance produced by the body and ingested in food

9 A sensation that often precedes a seizure

10 Protein produced by the body to fight infection or illness

Activity 10: Content Review

When responding to a fire, what do the following acronyms stand for?

1. R. A. C. E.

R. _____

A. _____

C. _____

E. _____

2. P. A. S. S.

P. _____

A. _____

S. _____

S. _____

Documentation and Core Nursing Skills

Activity 1: True or False

Beside each statement, write T for TRUE or F for FALSE.

1. _____ A resident's medical record belongs to their family.

2. _____ The care plan is another name for the medical record.

3. _____ Physical and occupational therapists may add information to a resident's chart.

4. _____ Some facilities use words and symbols on resident's door cards to communicate important information.

5. _____ Hunches are based on factual information.

6. _____ "This resident is 5'4" tall," is a subjective statement.

7. _____ Good observations should include detailed objective and subjective information.

8. _____ A nurse assistant plays a vital role in the gathering information about a resident's condition.

9. _____ The least important assessment tool a facility uses is the Resident Assessment Instrument (RAI).

10. _____ The RAI must be completed for all Medicare/Medicaid residents.

11. _____ An oral thermometer should not be used when a resident is paralyzed on one side of his mouth or cannot

     hold the thermometer in place.

12. _____ The nurse assistant can change the care plan whenever he/she feels it is necessary.

13. _____ Routine reporting is usually done just before the charge nurse goes to lunch.

14. _____ It is important for you to watch for changes in your residents' health.

15. _____ You should know your facility's policies on documentation before you chart in a resident's medical record.

Activity 2: Spell It Out

Using the word list below and the definition provided in each example, complete the spelling of the term.

Baseline   Body Mass Index (BMI)   Policy
Protocol   Respiration   Temperature
Tympanic temperature Vital signs   Objective information
Subjective information

1. Necessary for life: temperature, pulse, respiration and blood pressure:

____ I ____ ____ ____   ____ ____ G ____ ____

2. A degree of heat that naturally occurs in the body:

____ ____ ____ ____ E ____ ____ ____ ____ ____ E

3. The exchange of oxygen and carbon dioxide between the body cells:

____ ____ ____ P ____ R ____ ____ ____ ____ ____

4. Information based on an assumption, opinion, or on what the resident says about how they feel:

____ ____ B ____ ____ ____ T ____ ____ ____ ____   ____ ____ F ____ ____ M ____ ____ ____ ____ N

5. Beginning observations used for later comparisons: ____ ____ S ____ ____ ____ N ____

6. A measurement of a person's body fat: ____ ____ ____ ____   ____ ____ S ____   ____ N ____ ____ ____

7. A high-level plan for meeting goals, an acceptable procedure: ____ ____ ____ I ____ ____

8. A measurement of temperature of the eardrum:

____ ____ ____ P ____ ____ ____ ____ ____   ____ ____ M ____ ____ ____ ____ ____ ____ ____ E

9. Factual information gathered through observation:

____ B ____ ____ C ____ ____ ____ ____ ____   ____ ____ ____ O ____ ____ A ____ ____ ____ ____ ____

10. A facility's official way of doing something, usually put in writing: ____ ____ O ____ ____ C ____ ____

Activity 3: Situation and Response

Match each situation with the appropriate response.

Situation

1. __D__ Your co-worker has to leave early and asks you to document her residents' conditions.

2. __F__ A resident has made plans to go out to dinner with her family. You're not sure if any forms should be filled out.

3. __A__ A resident's roommate reports that the resident slipped off the toilet. The resident says "I didn't fall all the way to the floor and I'm okay!" You don't see any bruising or injuries.

4. __B__ You have just written a lengthy progress note in a resident's chart when you realize it's the wrong chart.

5. __C__ You have just told a resident they have orders to go to physical therapy BID. They stare at you and appear confused.

6. __E__ You are asked to participate in a resident's care planning meeting.

Response

A. Ask the resident for more details about what happened. Report all this information to the charge nurse so that the right actions can be taken.

B. Draw a single line through the incorrect word or entry. Print "Void, or Mistaken Entry" above or beside the incorrect word or entry and add the date and your initials above the entry.

C. Repeat your statement using simple terms: "Your doctor wants you to go to physical therapy twice today."

D. You are only allowed to document your own actions and observations. Remind your co-worker that it is illegal for you to document for anyone else.

E. You share your thoughts, ideas, and suggestions in a tactful and respectful manner.

F. Every facility should have a policy and procedure document about residents leaving the facility. Obtain a copy of the policy and follow each step correctly.

Activity 4: Word Scramble

History and Physical Examination

Unscramble the words in the space provided.

Allergies	Auscultation	Blood pressure	Date of birth
Draping	Height and weight	Inspection	Medical and surgical history
Objective information	Palpation	Percussion	Pulse
Respiratory rate	Subjective information	Temperature	Vital signs

1. EOBTJCEVI NNMFRTAOIIO _____

2. CJSVITEBEU TNIIORFMANO _____

3. EDAT FO IRTBH _____

4. DCLIEMA ADN GCURSAIL ISRYOTH _____

5. AIGLERLES _____

6. DPINARG _____

7. ILVTA SGSNI _____

8. TGIHEH ADN GITEWH _____

9. PNNOECIIST _____

10. LAIOTANPP _____

11. PCEOSSINUR _____

12. OTLAIUTAUCSN _____

13. REUEPTTMERA _____

14. ESULP _____

15. BODOL RSURSPEE _____

16. EASPOIRTRYR ARTE _____

Activity 5: Multiple Choice

Circle the letter beside the correct answer.

1. Just before placing a thermometer in a resident's mouth, what should you do?
   A. Dip it in a strong disinfectant.
   B. Hold it under hot running water.
   C. Wipe it on your sleeve or a clean gown.
   D. Place a disposable covering over the probe.

2. Mrs. Buckland's pulse is slow every time you check it. What could cause her to have a slow pulse?
   A. Being angry.
   B. Being relaxed.
   C. Being excited.
   D. Recent exercise.

3. Diastolic pressure is a measure of:
   A. Pressure inside a tank of oxygen.
   B. Pressure inside the facility's water heater.
   C. Pressure in the artery when the heart is at rest.
   D. Pressure in the artery when a person is running.

4. Why does facility staff take a medical history?
   A. To learn about the resident.
   B. To create a care plan.
   C. To get to know the family.
   D. To understand their favorite food.

5. A systematic approach during a physical exam uses:
   A. Both subjective and objective information about a residents' health.
   B. Make sure the resident has given you all their information.
   C. Let staff feel they have done a good job.
   D. See if the person's family has communicated all necessary details.

Activity 6: Matching

Match the personnel or department with the role they have in admitting a resident.

Personnel/Department

1. _____ Admission coordinator

2. _____ Dietary department

3. _____ Front office

4. _____ Housekeeping department

5. _____ Maintenance department

6. _____ Nurses

7. _____ Social worker

Role

A. Help the family with financial issues; sometimes may admit new residents.

B. Primary responsibility for admitting a new resident.

C. Clean and set up the room.

D. Help with move in; may set up phone for new resident.

E. Set up payment schedules.

F. Interview residents to find out their food preferences.

G. Start the assessment process; obtain and confirm all health care provider's orders.

Activity 7: True or False
Admission and Discharge

Beside each statement, write T for True or F for False.

1. _____ A nurse assistant can make a dramatic difference in a new resident's adjustment to the facility.

2. _____ A new resident can bring in personal items such as photos, plants, and wall hangings.

3. _____ After a resident has lived at the facility for a week or so, staff no longer needs to knock on their door before entering.

4. _____ A draw sheet is used as a temporary screen when a resident's privacy curtain is being washed.

5. _____ If you find that a call light is not working properly, you should report it immediately.

6. _____ Discharge from a nursing facility is often a happy occasion for a resident and their family.

Activity 8: Matching

Match the term to the definition.

Definition	Term
1. _____ Evaluation of a patient or condition	A. Diastolic pressure
2. _____ System that enables residents to signal that they need assistance from staff	B. Pulse
3. _____ Number that reflects the pressure when the heart is at rest between beats	C. Call system
4. _____ Measurement that estimates the percentage of fat tissue in the body	D. Respiration
5. _____ High blood pressure	E. Face sheet
6. _____ Low blood pressure	F. Hypotension
7. _____ Number that reflects the pressure in the artery when the heart is pumping	G. Protocol
8. _____ An official or standard way of doing something, usually put in writing	H. Assessment
9. _____ Exchange of oxygen and carbon dioxide between the atmosphere and body cells; breathing	I. Vital signs
10. _____ Measurements of temperature, pulse, respiration, and blood pressure	J. Hypertension
11. _____ Measure of heart rate taken by feeling the expansion of an artery as blood is pushed through when the heart contracts	K. Body mass index (bmi)
12. _____ One-page summary of important information about a patient/resident	L. Systolic pressure

Activity 9: Free Response

List five ways a nurse assistant can help a new resident feel comfortable about being in a nursing facility.

1. _____
   _____
   _____

2. _____
   _____
   _____

3. _____
   _____
   _____

4. _____
   _____
   _____

5. _____
   _____
   _____

List two fears a resident could have when they are being discharged to a less restrictive setting or home.

1. _____
   _____

2. _____
   _____

Positioining, Moving, and Restorative Care

Activity 1: Crossword

Adapt
Hypotension
Mobility
Transfer

Fowler's position
Independent
Positioning

Fragile
Limb
Supine

Across

4 Easily broken or destroyed, delicate

6 Capable or moving or being moved

8 Reduced blood flow when sitting or standing causing dizziness

9 Act of placing or arranging

10 Move a resident from one surface to another (chair to bed)

Down

1 Lying on the back when the head of the bed is raised 30-90 degrees (usually about 45 degrees)

2 Change to fit new conditions

3 Not subject to control by others, not dependent

5 Lying on the back

7 Arm or leg

Activity 2: True or False

Beside each statement, write T for True or F for False.

1. __T__ Someone who has been in bed even for a short time may feel stiff or weak.

2. __T__ If you don't know a resident well, you should get help before transferring them.

3. __T__ You should never use side rails when moving or positioning a resident.

4. __F__ A resident is supine if they are sitting up straight.

5. __F__ If you position a wheelchair up against a wall, it does not need to be locked.

6. __F__ Postural hypotension causes blood to pool in the brain.

7. __T__ It is important to have a resident sit up at the side of the bed before transferring them to a chair.

8. __T__ A mechanical lift is used to transfer a resident without the assistance of a co-worker.

Activity 3: Situation and Response

Read each situation. In the space provided, write the letter of the appropriate response to that situation.

Situation

1. __D__ Mrs. Saunders has left sided weakness. You have to transfer her out of a wheelchair onto the toilet.

2. __A__ You notice that Mrs. Walters has slumped down in her chair. She is unable to pull herself back up to a comfortable position.

3. __E__ Mr. Hudson has been in bed with the flu for several days. He wants to get up and walk to the bathroom.

4. __B__ Mrs. Adamson has been lying on her back for almost two hours. You need to reposition her.

5. __C__ You have transferred Mrs. Adjani from the bed to a chair. She says she is comfortable, but you notice that her feet don't touch the floor.

Response

A. Place a gait belt around her waist. Standing on either side of the resident, have a co-worker assist you by pulling up on the belt with one hand and lifting the resident's knees with the other hand.

B. Place her in a side-lying position. Stand on the side to which you will turn her. With a hand on her shoulder and the other on her hip, help her turn toward you. Position her head, neck arms, and legs comfortably.

C. Place a stool or pillow under her feet so that her knees and hips are at the same height.

D. Position the wheelchair so that her strong side is closest to the toilet. Lock the wheels, raise the footrests, apply gait belt, and assist her with a stand pivot transfer.

E. To prevent dizziness, have him roll onto his side and then sit at the edge of the bed with his legs dangling for a few minutes.

Activity 4: Multiple Choice

Circle the letter beside the correct answer.

1. Why is it important to be careful when transferring a resident who has osteoporosis from a bed to a chair?
   A. A resident with osteoporosis is prone to weakness.
   B. Residents who have osteoporosis get dizzy very quickly.
   C. Residents with osteoporosis are at risk for breaking bones.
   D. Sometimes blood can pool in their extremities and cause confusion.

2. You are walking Mrs. Reynolds down the hall when she becomes faint and begins to fall. What is the BEST way to prevent her from injuring herself?
   A. Pin her against the wall until a co-worker arrives.
   B. Put both arms around her and drag her to a nearby chair.
   C. Holding on to her gait belt, help her sit down on the floor.
   D. Grab hold of her hair to prevent her head from hitting the floor.

3. You are assisting a co-worker as they move a resident up in a chair. Where will your hands be positioned?
   A. One hand on the gait belt, one under their buttocks.
   B. One hand under the resident's knee, the other under their arm.
   C. One hand on the gait belt, the other hand under the resident's knee.
   D. One hand under the resident's arm, the other hand around the resident's ankle.

4. Mrs. Desmond has a hip fracture. You have reminded her that she shouldn't cross her legs, but she forgets. How can you prevent her from re-injuring her hip?
   A. Transfer her back to the bed.
   B. Put a pillow between her legs.
   C. Suggest she stand instead of sit.
   D. Call her doctor to report the problem.

5. When you position a resident on their back, their legs should normally be positioned:
   A. With a pillow between them.
   B. As close together as possible.
   C. With both legs straight and slightly apart.
   D. With one leg straight and one leg slightly bent.

Activity 5: Independent or Dependent

Read the following sentences. In the space provided, write I if the action promotes INDEPENDENCE or D if it promotes DEPENDENCE.

1. _____ A resident wants to walk to the dining room, but you tell him you can get him there quicker by pushing him in a wheelchair.

2. _____ You give a resident a bed bath even though with assistance they could take a shower.

3. _____ You encourage a resident to take a walk while you make the bed.

4. _____ You wheel a resident to the activities room.

5. _____ You encourage a resident to use his cane to take a walk.

6. _____ You say to a resident, "I'll start buttoning your shirt, and you can finish it."

7. _____ A resident can walk a little, but you use a wheelchair instead of allowing them to walk.

8. _____ A resident picks up a spoon to eat, but because they are slow you take the spoon and begin feeding them.

9. _____ You hand a piece of bread to a resident who is recovering from a stroke, encouraging them to use their weak hand.

10. _____ You discuss a resident's eating limitations with the charge nurse in hopes of coming up with some assistive devices so they can eat without your help.

Activity 6: Content Review

List two examples in each category of equipment. Refer to your textbook if necessary.

Assistive devices

1. _____
2. _____

Prosthetic and orthotic devices

1. _____
2. _____

Positioning devices

1. _____
2. _____

Aids for activities of daily living

1. _____
2. _____

Activity 7: Multiple Choice

Circle the letter beside the correct answer.

1. You are working with a resident who recently had a stroke. It takes the resident a long time to dress himself. How can you help him regain lost function?
    A. Insist on doing everything for him.
    B. Tell the family to help him every day.
    C. Help him so that he gets dressed faster.
    D. Be patient and let him do as much as he can.

2. The nurse asks you to give range-of-motion exercise to Mrs. White, who is confined to bed. According to her care plan, there are no restrictions. What does "no restrictions" mean?
    A. You should work her joints and muscles very hard.
    B. Provide ROM exercise as often as possible on each shift.
    C. Mrs. White should be able to do all of the exercises herself.
    D. You may move each joint through its full available range.

3. Mrs. Wilson seems puzzled or confused when you tell her you'd like her to practice using a walker. How can you help her understand?
    A. Tell her you are in a hurry.
    B. Repeat the request in a different way.
    C. Use baby talk to get your point across.
    D. Tell the next shift nurse assistant to try it.

4. Which of the following is an orthotic device?
    A. Walker
    B. Trapeze
    C. Leg brace
    D. Artificial leg

5. You are about to help Mrs. Paulsen take a walk. She is on oxygen. What is the BEST way to ensure her safety?
    A. Have her take a few deep breaths before you walk.
    B. Carry her oxygen tank under your arm as you walk.
    C. Take her off oxygen for the short time she is walking.
    D. Ask another staff to follow and pull a portable oxygen tank.

Activity 8: Fill in the Blank

Using the terms provided below, complete each sentence correctly.

Alert   Artificial limb   Capability
Cuing   Function   Immobilized
Independence   Maintain   Optimal
Prompting   Regain   Stump

1. The portion of an extremity remaining after the rest is removed is called the _____Stump_____.

2. In order to keep something in its existing state, it is necessary to _____Maintain_____.

3. Restorative activities are done in a way to help restore _____function_____, or the action for which the body part is used.

4. If someone is quick to perceive and act on a situation, they are _____alert_____.

5. When you give a resident a signal to begin a specific speech or action, you are _____cuing_____.

6. Moving a person to take an action, or helping them remember something is called _____prompting_____.

7. In order to prevent freedom of movement, a joint or body part must be _____immobilized_____.

8. The goal of restorative activities is to help a resident achieve their most desirable, or _____optimal_____, level of functioning.

9. An arm or leg that is human-made is called a(n) _____artifical_____ _____limb_____.

10. _____Capability_____ refers to a person's ability to do something.

11. A person who is not subject to control by others has _____independence_____.

12. Restorative activities can help a person _____regain_____ lost function again.

Activity 9: Matching

Match the term to the definition.

Term

1. _____ Brace

2. _____ Extremity

3. _____ Orthotic device

4. _____ Prosthetic device

5. _____ Rehabilitation

6. _____ Reinforce

7. _____ Restorative

8. _____ Splint

9. _____ Trapeze

Definition

A. Device that supports and strengthens a body part

B. Supportive equipment made for a resident, such as a brace or splint that supports a limb

C. A limb of the body

D. Device made to replace a missing body part or function

E. The process of restoring to a former state

F. Device to use to support or immobilize a body part

G. A short horizontal bar suspended by two parallel ropes, used to pull oneself up in bed

H. To strengthen something

I. Restore to a former state

Activity 10: True or False

Beside each statement, write T for True or F for False.

1. __T__ A contracture occurs when a joint becomes stuck in a certain position.

2. __F__ Once the interdisciplinary team sets goals for a resident, those goals never change.

3. __F__ A disability is a physical problem only and never affects a resident's psychological state.

4. __F__ Prompting and cuing are forms of sign language used only to communicate with hearing impaired individuals.

5. __T__ One goal of restorative activities is to enable a resident to perform activities of daily living independently.

6. __F__ An entire ROM exercise program always takes about 60 minutes.
   15

7. __T__ You perform finger flexion when you bend the fingers at each of the joints.

8. __T__ Each range of motion exercise should be repeated 5 to 10 times, depending on the resident's comfort level and care plan.

Activity 11: Content Review

In the column to the left, list five effects that could occur if a resident is confined to the bed. In the right column, list the body system that is involved in the effect.

Effect   Body System

1. _____   _____

2. _____   _____

3. _____   _____

4. _____   _____

5. _____   _____

Activity 12: In Your Own Words

1. Have you had to sit or lie absolutely still for a long time? How did it feel?

   _____

   _____

   _____

   _____

2. Would you feel embarrassed if caretakers had to use a mechanical lift to get you out of bed?

   _____

   _____

   _____

   _____

3. Have you ever fallen on the ice or while playing a game? Did it hurt? Did it make you more cautious?

   _____

   _____

   _____

   _____

4. When would it be proper to leave a resident who has fallen alone?

   _____

   _____

   _____

   _____

Nutrition

Activity 1: Multiple Choice

Circle the letter beside the correct answer.

1. **Why is it important to "liberalize" therapeutic diets?**
   A. So that they will be more nutritious.
   B. Therapeutic diets contain too much sugar.
   C. Therapeutic diets are generally too low in calories.
   D. A person may not eat as much if their diet is too restricted.

2. **Renal diets often restrict:**
   A. Fats.
   B. Fiber.
   C. Sugar.
   D. Protein.

3. **As you distribute meals to residents, you should check to see if:**
   A. Each tray has a bud vase and flower.
   B. Each meal includes a serving of red meat.
   C. Each tray has the right diet for the resident.
   D. Each meal has only fat-free, sugar-free desserts.

4. **What happens when a person aspirates their food?**
   A. They feel like taking a nap.
   B. They throw up their dinner.
   C. They feel the need to belch.
   D. They may develop pneumonia.

5. **Which of the following signs is an indication of dehydration?**
   A. Sunken eyes.
   B. Good skin turgor.
   C. Alzheimer's disease.
   D. Frequent trips to the bathroom.

6. **In order to stay hydrated, a resident must:**
   A. Avoid sweet foods.
   B. Keep out of the sun.
   C. Drink plenty of fluids.
   D. Bathe or shower each day.

Activity 2: Fill in the Blank

Complete each sentence adding the correct term.

Dehydration   Dysphagia   Esophagus
Hydration   Nutrition   Sodium
Supplements   Turgor

1. _____ can occur if a resident does not have adequate fluid intake.

2. Tight skin that does not "tent" has _____ which is a sign of good hydration.

3. The act of nourishing or being nourished is called _____.

4. Maintaining an adequate fluid level in the body is _____.

5. _____ is also called salt.

6. Someone who has difficulty chewing or swallowing food has a condition known as _____.

7. The _____ is a muscular tube that leads from the mouth to the stomach.

8. Residents who need additional nutrition may receive it in concentrated amounts through

_____.

Activity 3: Content Review
Special Diets

Write the answers in the space provided. Refer to the textbook if necessary.

Why would residents be placed on the following diets?

1. Calorie-restricted diet:

   _____

   _____

2. Sodium-restricted diet:

   _____

   _____

3. Fat/cholesterol-restricted diet:

   _____

   _____

4. Protein-restricted diet:

   _____

   _____

5. Why would a resident need supplements?

   _____

   _____

6. What is your role as a nurse assistant in assisting residents with meals?

   _____

   _____

   _____

Activity 4: Situation and Response

Match the situation with the appropriate response by a nurse assistant. Some responses will be used more than once.

Situation

1. _____ A resident tells you they cannot cut their meat.

2. _____ You check a resident's water pitcher and find that it is full.

3. _____ A resident ate only 25% of their meal.

4. _____ You pass trays out to residents.

5. _____ A resident tells you they are thirsty.

6. _____ A resident cannot open their milk carton.

7. _____ A tray arrives without utensils.

8. _____ You are serving a new resident.

9. _____ A resident says they have the wrong tray.

10. _____ A resident refuses to eat anything you offer.

Response

A. Assist the resident.

B. Report this to the charge nurse.

C. Obtain the missing item.

D. Offer the resident water.

E. Check the tray card and the resident's ID band.

Activity 5: True or False

Beside each statement, write T for True or F for False.

1. _____ The food service department provides support with finances.

2. _____ A resident's nutritional status can be enhanced with a combination of correct diet and proper assistance from

   the nurse assistant.

3. _____ All residents are given a therapeutic diet.

4. _____ A calorie-restricted diet is usually ordered for diabetics.

5. _____ A resident who has difficulty swallowing has aphasia.

6. _____ The food service department uses a feeding tube to mix foods.

7. _____ Intake is the measurement of food and fluids a resident takes in.

8. _____ A nurse assistant measures a resident's weight just to have something to talk about with family members.

9. _____ It is critical to monitor a resident's fluid intake and output.

10. _____ You should notify the charge nurse immediately if a resident's weight drops 1 pound in two months.

Activity 6: Convert the Amounts

Using these formulas, convert the following serving amounts to cc.

1 ounce (oz) = 30 cc
1 cup = 240 cc

1. A 4 oz serving of orange juice = _____ cc.

2. A 6 oz serving of coffee = _____ cc.

3. A 1/2 cup of Jell-O = _____ cc.

4. A tumbler containing 1 1/2 cups of iced tea = _____ cc.

5. A 3 oz serving of ice cream = _____ cc.

6. An 8 oz bowl of soup = _____ cc.

Activity 7: Content Review

Food Groups

List the five food groups and provide examples from each group.

1. _____

   _____

   _____

2. _____

   _____

   _____

   _____

3. _____

   _____

   _____

   _____

4. _____

   _____

   _____

   _____

5. _____

   _____

   _____

   _____

Elimination

Activity 1: Dignity Checklist

Read each statement and indicate if the nurse assistant protected the resident's dignity. In the space provided, write D if the resident's DIGNITY is protected or N if it is NOT PROTECTED.

1. __D__ You respond to a resident's call light immediately.

2. __D__ You close the door before helping the resident use a bedpan.

3. __N__ You tease the resident about wetting herself.

4. __N__ You discuss a resident's bowel problems in front of their roommate's family.

5. __N__ You left the resident sitting on the toilet for 30 minutes.

6. __D__ You talk in private with a resident about their elimination pattern.

7. __N__ You leave a stool sample on the desk, with the resident's name clearly marked on the label.

Activity 2: Crossword

Bladder
Bowel
Elimination
Gastrointestinal
Incontinence
Occult
Ostomy
Parasite
Stoma
Stool
Urinate
Urine
Void

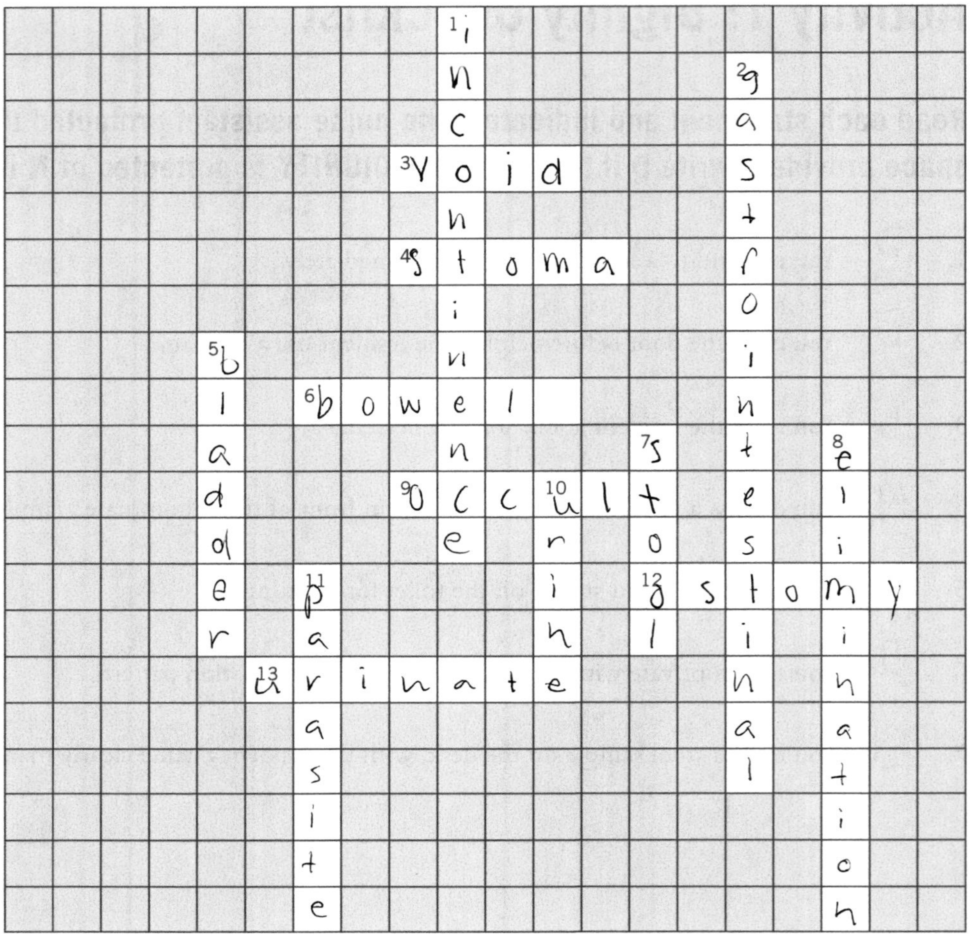

The crossword grid answers:

- 1 Down: incontinence
- 2 Down: gastrointestinal
- 3 Across: void
- 4 Across: stoma
- 5 Down: bladder
- 6 Across: bowel
- 7 Down: stool
- 8 Down: elimination
- 9 Across: occult
- 10 Down: urine
- 11 Down: parasite
- 12 Across: ostomy
- 13 Across: urinate

Across

3 To eliminate liquid waste from the body
4 A surgically created opening
6 Refers to the large and small intestines
9 Refers to blood that is present in stool that cannot be seen
12 Surgical opening from the intestine to outside the body
13 To pass urine

Down

1 Inability to hold urine or stool is called
2 Related to the stomach and intestines
5 Sac inside the body that holds urine
7 Human waste, or feces, from the bowel
8 The process of ridding the body of urine and stool
10 Waste liquid secreted by the kidney
11 An organism that lives in or on another organism

Activity 3: Yes or No

For each situation, write Y for YES if it should be reported to the charge nurse, or N for NO if you would not report it.

1. __Y__ The resident's urine had a foul odor.

2. __Y__ The resident had a painful, hard, black stool today.

3. __Y__ The resident complained of painful urination.

4. __Y__ The resident's stool had red blood in it.

5. __N__ The resident urinated two times during your shift.

6. __Y__ The resident was incontinent for the first time.

7. __N__ The resident drank two cups of coffee during your shift.

8. __Y__ The resident's abdomen is swollen, and they have not had a bowel movement in two days.

9. __N__ The resident's urine was clear.

10. __Y__ The resident had a watery, foul-smelling stool today.

Activity 4: Labeling

Match each photo with the name of the item. In the space provided, write the letter found next to the photo.

A. Urinal   B. Bedside Commode   C. Fracture pan   D. Bedpan

1. _____

2. _____

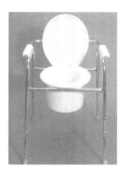

3. _____

4. _____

Activity 5: Matching

Match the term to the correct definition.

A. Functional incontinence   _____   The goal of this program is to prompt the resident to void at intervals short enough to prevent leakage.

B. Habit training   _____   Occurs when pressure is put on the bladder like coughing, sneezing, laughing, lifting or exercising. Small amounts of urine leak.

C. Mixed incontinence   _____   Is a sudden strong urge to urinate, followed by urinary leakage. You may have a resident that rushes to the bathroom but doesn't make it on time and has an accident.

D. Prompted voiding   _____   The goal of this program is to regain control of the bladder by gradually lengthening the intervals between times the resident voids.

E. Stress incontinence   _____   Is a combination of stress and urge incontinence. Your resident may report that they feel a sudden urge to urinate and leaks when they laugh or sneeze.

F. Overflow incontinence   _____   Occurs when the bladder doesn't fully empty causing constant or frequent dribbling. Your resident may report that they are "always wet" and requires frequent clothing changes.

G. Urge incontinence   _____   Occurs due to a physical or cognitive limitation. The resident may require assist to get to the bathroom due to a broken leg but doesn't get assistance in time.

H. Bladder retraining   _____   Involves documenting a resident's elimination patterns for at least three days to determine the resident's voiding habits.

Activity 6: Content Review

What are some factors that contribute to incontinence?

_____

_____

_____

_____

List at least three goals when caring for an incontinent resident.

1. _____

2. _____

3. _____

Describe the difference between a colostomy and ileostomy.

_____

_____

_____

_____

What can you do as a nurse aide to promote dignity when assisting with elimination?

_____

_____

_____

_____

Provide at least three examples of how to you can support regular elimination with your resident's.

1. _____

2. _____

3. _____

Aging and Chronic Disease Management

Activity 1: Matching

The Body Systems

Match the Body System to the correct definition.

Body System	Definition

1. _____ Circulatory System

A. Body system made up of the skin, nails, and hair

2. _____ Digestive System

B. Body system made up of bones, muscles, tendons, ligaments, and joints

3. _____ Endocrine System

C. Body system that includes the heart, blood vessels, and lymphatic tissues and vessels

4. _____ Integumentary System

D. Body system made up of the brain, spinal cord, and nerves

5. _____ Musculoskeletal System

E. Body system involved in processing food, providing nutrients to the body, and expelling waste

6. _____ Nervous System

F. Body system that allows for the exchange of oxygen and carbon dioxide in the body

7. _____ Reproductive System

H. Body system that helps maintain fluid balance and eliminates liquid waste

8. _____ Respiratory System

I. Body system made up of reproductive organs and glands

9. _____ Urinary System

G. Body system made up of glands that secrete hormones

Activity 2: Multiple Choice

Circle the letter beside the correct answer.

1. A resident who wakes up with swelling and pain in their arthritic knees has:
   A. A symptom of an acute infection.
   B. A compromised immune system.
   C. An acute condition in a chronic phase.
   D. A chronic condition in an acute phase.

2. What is a silent infection?
   A. An infection that lasts a long time.
   B. An infection with dramatic symptoms.
   C. An infection that does not respond to treatment.
   D. An infection that can only be detected through lab tests.

3. Which body system is responsible for maintaining fluid balance and eliminating liquid wastes?
   A. The urinary system.
   B. The nervous system.
   C. The integumentary system.
   D. The musculoskeletal system.

4. How does the circulatory system change with aging?
   A. Brain cells die.
   B. Muscle strength decreases.
   C. Blood vessels become more rigid and stiff.
   D. Chest wall and lung structures become more rigid.

5. The signs and symptoms of cataracts include:
   A. Hearing loss.
   B. Problems with glare.
   C. Blindness in both eyes.
   D. Heightened color sensitivity.

Activity 3: Matching

Match the nurse assistant's task with the preventative strategy.

Condition

1. _____ Helping an immobile resident maintain good circulation.

2. _____ Being attentive to any changes in the resident's skin condition.

3. _____ Encouraging a resident to eat their meals.

4. _____ Helping an incontinent resident to stay clean and dry.

5. _____ Assisting a resident to ambulate.

6. _____ Telling the charge nurse about changes to a resident's skin.

Preventative Strategy

A. Mobility

B. Nutrition

C. Observation

D. Range-of-motion (ROM) exercise

E. Bathing/moisturizing

F. Reporting

Activity 4: Multiple choice

Circle the letter beside the correct answer.

1. **Skin that has integrity is:**
    A. Tanned, tough, and thick.
    B. Free of moles or birthmarks.
    C. Free of cuts, bruises, or wounds.
    D. Only found on babies and children.

2. **What is a pressure injury?**
    A. A stomach ulcer that is caused by stress.
    B. An ulcer appearing only in people with AIDS.
    C. A wound that appears in pressure areas of the skin.
    D. An ulcer of the lips or mouth that is caused by a virus.

3. **Shearing occurs when:**
    A. You tear a sheet as you are making a bed.
    B. You put too much alcohol on a razor burn.
    C. Skin rubs against an object or another area of skin.
    D. A resident's skin remains damp for hours at a time.

4. **Circulation of blood to the skin is enhanced by:**
    A. Eating.
    B. Talking.
    C. Walking.
    D. Sleeping.

5. **You can help maintain a resident's skin by:**
    A. Inspecting it carefully every day.
    B. Taking them outside on sunny days.
    C. Giving them a daily dose of castor oil.
    D. Rubbing it hourly with antibiotic ointment.

Activity 5: Spell It Out

Conditions of the Skin

Using the terms provided below, spell out each word beside the correct description.

Blister   Epidermis   Mole

Dermatitis   Integumentary   Subcutaneous

Dermis   Malignant   Wart

1. A colored spot in the body: ____ ____ L ____

2. Refers to a tumor or condition that tends to spread abnormal cells:

    ____ ____ L ____ G ____ ____ ____ ____

3. The top or first layer of the skin: E ____ ____ ____ ____ ____ ____ ____ S

4. An elevated area of epidermis containing watery liquid: ____ ____ ____ S ____ E ____

5. The second layer of skin: ____ ____ ____ M ____ ____

6. The body system made up of the skin, nails, and hair:

    ____ ____ T ____ ____ ____ ____ ____ ____ ____ ____ R ____

7. Under the skin: ____ ____ B ____ ____ ____ ____ ____ ____ ____ ____ S

8. A horny bump on the skin caused by a virus: ____ A ____ ____

9. Inflammation of the skin: ____ ____ R ____ ____ ____ ____ T ____ ____

Activity 6: True or False

Beside each statement, write T for TRUE or F for FALSE.

1. _____ Even if a person is born with healthy skin, they are at risk for pressure injuries when they are elderly.

2. _____ Only a nurse or doctor can identify redness on the skin.

3. _____ An overweight person can't develop pressure injuries.

4. _____ ROM exercises can improve circulation.

5. _____ As a nurse assistant, you are in the best position to observe the resident's skin from head to toe.

6. _____ Daily inspection of the skin is an excellent way to prevent pressure injuries.

7. _____ Stage IV pressure injuries should be treated only with daily bathing.

8. _____ A resident is at high risk for skin breakdown if they cannot go to the toilet by themselves.

9. _____ Stage I pressure injuries have a foul smell or discharge.

10. _____ Active people are at greater risk for skin breakdown.

11. _____ Cornstarch should be applied to a stage III pressure injury.

12. _____ Adequate nutrition and fluid intake are required for healthy skin.

13. _____ Bed sore is another term for pressure injury.

14. _____ If you think a change in a resident's skin isn't serious, then you don't need to report it.

15. _____ Shearing force can occur when you slide a resident across their bed.

Activity 7: Labeling

Label the following photos of pressure injuries correctly. (Which is Stage I, II, III, or IV?)

1. _____

3. _____

2. _____

4. _____

Activity 8: Situation and Response

Match the situation with the correct response.

Situation

1. _____ Mrs. Leamus has thin, delicate skin. You notice that her thighs tend to stick to the toilet seat.

2. _____ Mr. Mundt has a scratch on his elbow. It was caused by rough spot on the arm rest of his wheelchair.

3. _____ Mrs. Guillam is confined to bed. She is being treated for a stage II pressure injury on her right heel.

4. _____ Mrs. Crail is confused, underweight, and has little interest in food. When she sleeps, she tends to thrash around in bed, pulling at the sheets and covers.

5. _____ Mr. Karden is incontinent and wears an incontinence brief.

Response

A. Encourage the resident to eat all their meals and drink plenty of fluids. Inspect the resident's skin daily. Be sure the bed linens are free of wrinkles before the resident goes to sleep.

B. Follow the charge nurse's instructions for treatment of the problem. Check frequently to see that the resident's heel is not resting on the bed.

C. Assist resident to the toilet on a frequent basis. When the resident wets themselves, clean their perineal area with soap and water before putting on a clean incontinence brief.

D. Inspect the resident's thighs for skin breakdown. Use cornstarch on the toilet seat to prevent shearing. Notify the charge nurse about the situation.

E. Ask the charge nurse what to do about the scratch. Place a pillow between the resident's arm and the armrest until the rough spot can be removed from the armrest.

Activity 9: Fill in the Blank
Wound Care

Complete each sentence using the correct term.

Contusion   Puncture

Incision   Lesion

Laceration

1. A(n) _____ is made by a sharp instrument or object.

2. A type of wound down into the skin, made by something pointed is called a(n) _____.

3. A(n) _____ is a type of wound made by blunt force, causing bruising and swelling, but usually the skin is not broken.

4. A wound caused by a disease such as cancer, HIV, or poor circulation is called a(n) _____ or skin breakdown.

5. A(n) _____ is a type of wound made by an object causing an irregular, jagged wound.

Activity 10: Fill in the Blank

Complete each sentence using the correct term.

Arthritis
Fracture
Muscle atrophy
Musculoskeletal system

Osteoarthritis
Osteoporosis
Rheumatoid arthritis

1. Inflammation that causes pain and limits movement in affected joints is called _____.

2. _____ is another term for a broken bone.

3. The _____ _____ is made up of bones, muscles, tendons, ligaments, and joints.

4. Joint inflammation caused by "wear and tear" of the joint is called _____.

5. A condition in which bones become weak and brittle due to loss of minerals, especially calcium, is called

   _____.

6. _____ _____ is an autoimmune inflammatory joint disease.

7. When muscle wastes away, it is known as _____ _____.

Activity 11: Matching

Match the term to the definition.

Definition

A. Lung infection

B. Body system that takes in oxygen (inhale) and expels carbon dioxide (exhale)

C. Air sacs in the lungs

D. Chronic inflammatory disease of bronchial passages and lungs; three most common types of disease are bronchitis, emphysema, and asthma

E. Health problem that begins rapidly

F. Right and left airway structures to the lungs

G. A bluish or purplish discoloration of the skin caused by deficient oxygenation of the blood

Term

1. _____ Alveoli

2. _____ Bronchi

3. _____ Chronic obstructive pulmonary disease

4. _____ Cyanosis

5. _____ Pneumonia

6. _____ Respiratory system

7. _____ Acute

Activity 12: Fill in the Blank

Complete each sentence using the correct term.

Arteries   Capillaries   Cerebral vascular accident
Circulatory system   Coronary artery disease   Congestive heart failure
Edema   Peripheral vascular disease   Veins

1. _____ _____ _____ is a
   condition that causes a diminished blood flow to the arms and legs.

2. The blood vessels that carry deoxygenated blood from the body back to the heart and lungs are called

   _____ .

3. _____ are tiny blood vessels that connect arteries and veins, where oxygen is
   exchanged for carbon dioxide inside organs.

4. The body system that includes the heart and blood vessels that carry oxygen and nutrients to the body and remove

   carbon dioxide is called the _____ .

5. _____ _____ _____ is a
   condition that results in reduced blood flow through the coronary arteries, which nourish the heart.

6. Fluid gain or retention, most commonly observed in the legs and ankles, is called _____ .

7. When the blood flow to the brain is interrupted (also called stroke), a(n) _____

   _____ _____ occurs.

8. _____ are blood vessels that carry oxygenated blood to all parts of the body.

9. _____ _____ _____ is a
   condition that occurs when the heart muscle weakens and the heart becomes ineffective in moving blood through
   the body.

Activity 13: Matching

Match the term to the definition.

Definition

A. A neurological disease that affects motor skills

B. Progressive disabling disease that affects nerve fibers

C. Body system made up of the brain, spinal cord, and nerves

Term

1. _____ Multiple sclerosis

2. _____ Nervous system

3. _____ Parkinson's disease

Activity 14: Spell It Out

Using the terms provided below, spell out each word beside the correct description.

Fallopian tubes
Ovaries
Penis
Reproductive

Uterus
Vagina
Vulva

1. A muscular canal in the female involved in sexual intercourse, childbirth, and passage of menstrual flow:

   ____ ____ G ____ ____ ____

2. Two tubes that carry egg cells from the ovaries to the uterus:

   ____ ____ L ____ ____ P ____ ____ ____   ____ ____ B ____ S

3. Organs in the female's pelvic area that secrete hormones involved in sexual function and becoming pregnant:

   ____ V ____ ____ ____ ____ ____

4. Body system that provides sexual pleasure and allows for human reproduction:

   ____ ____ P ____ ____ ____ ____ ____ ____ ____ V ____

5. The external structure of the female sex organs: ____ ____ ____ V ____

6. A muscular reproductive organ where the fetus develops during pregnancy; it sheds its lining during menstruation:

   ____ T ____ ____ ____ ____

7. Male organ of sexual intercourse and urination: ____ ____ ____ I ____

Advanced and Specialty Care Environments

Activity 1: Crossword Diabetic Care

Blood sugar   Feet   Finger prick
Glucose meter   Hyperglycemia   Hypoglycemia
Insulin

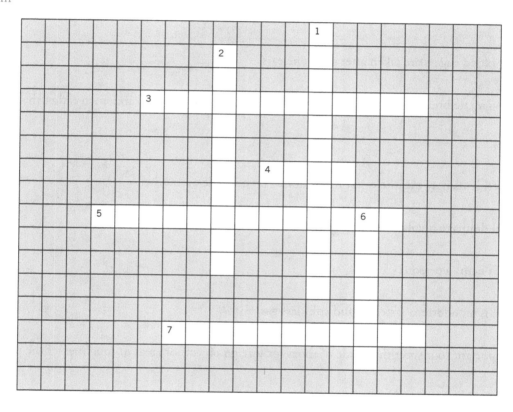

Across

3 Condition in which a person's blood sugar level may become too low

4 People with diabetes are at risk of problems with this part of the body

5 Condition in which a person's blood sugar may become too high

7 Common type of test of blood sugar

Down

1 Used to test blood sugar

2 This can be monitored by using a glucose meter

6 Diabetes is a problem with the body's ability to produce or use this

Activity 2: True or False

Beside each statement, write T for TRUE or F for FALSE.

1. _____ Heat or cold may be applied to the entire body for a general effect.

2. _____ Heat stops tissue from healing.

3. _____ People who are on a subacute floor usually need care for a long time.

4. _____ Fasting blood sugars are taken after someone eats.

5. _____ Diaphragmatic breathing is deep breathing that uses the muscles of the abdomen rather than the chest

   muscles.

6. _____ Some residents may breathe easier if positioned on one side or another.

7. _____ Postural drainage involves walking the resident every four hours.

8. _____ Hypoxia helps a person.

9. _____ Oxygen is an odorless, tasteless, and colorless gas.

10. _____ It is important to inspect the inside of shoes for foreign objects or areas of roughness if the person has

   diabetes.

Activity 3: Fill in the Blank
Preparing for Surgery

Complete each sentence using the correct term.

Anesthesia   Anesthetic   Elastic stockings

Emesis basin   Preoperative   Postoperative

Prosthesis   Splint

1. A(n) _____ is used to hold or keep an area from moving.

2. The time before surgery is called _____.

3. A state of being unaware or unable to feel is called _____.

4. A device that substitutes and functions in the place of a missing body part is called a(n) _____.

5. A(n) _____ _____ is a special basin used to catch vomit or secretions coughed up.

6. The time after surgery is called _____.

7. _____ is the medication given to a person before surgery.

8. _____ _____ are often worn after surgery to help prevent blood clots.

Activity 4: Pre-op Check List

Practice completing the pre-op checklist with a classmate or family member.

PRE-OP CHECK LIST
DEPARTMENT OF NURSING

Check List
This list must accompany each patient
Nurse preparing the patient must complete and sign checklist form
Nurse releasing the patient must verify the patient's id and sign form
List to be kept with patient's record until discharged then destroyed

Identification Bands	**Clinical data in chart** ( )	
A) Arm ( )	CBC	EKG if ordered
B) Leg ( )	Urinalysis	Blood set up as ordered
C) Allergy ( )	Chest X-ray	

Skin Preparations ( )	Medication charted ( )
Note abnormalities	Medication sheet sent w/patient ( )

Vital signs recorded ( )	**Record assembled** ( )	
Height and weight ( )	Current record	Medication sheet
Catheterized ( )	Old records	Vital signs sheets
Voided ( )	X-ray	Doctor's order sheet
Time _____	Other	
Amount _____		

Dress	Pre op orders reviewed ( )
A) Hospital gown ( )	Procedure consent ( )
B) Hair pins, wigs removed ( )	Anesthesia consent ( )
C) Nail polish removed ( )	

Valuable checklist	none	removed	not removed
1. Dentures upper	( )	( )	( )
lower	( )	( )	( )
2. Glasses	( )	( )	( )
3. Contacts	( )	( )	( )
4. Prosthetic-devises	( )	( )	( )
5. Jewelry/earrings	( )	( )	( )
6. Hearing aids	( )	( )	( )
7. Other	( )	( )	( )

_____   _____
Signature of Nurse Preparing Patient   Signature of Nurse Releasing Patient

Activity 5: Word Search
Communication techniques for residents with cognitive impairments

```
I  D  T  O  H  P  T  G  T  N  E  U  Q  A  H  B  P  E  C  P  A  G  B  S
S  O  T  P  M  V  F  X  M  G  N  I  K  A  E  P  S  B  G  S  I  E  T  F
Y  B  D  V  Z  B  P  W  N  S  Q  O  V  B  D  P  W  E  K  A  E  I  G  B
Y  W  Z  V  X  S  G  Q  I  C  S  K  J  Q  Y  E  P  I  K  E  A  I  A  L
G  T  X  S  U  J  S  K  L  N  B  Z  E  K  S  P  N  G  I  U  V  I  S  C
S  Z  D  W  E  Z  D  Q  G  H  T  A  Y  V  E  G  X  G  Y  I  L  H  N  L
T  S  O  T  L  E  N  C  B  T  S  I  H  Z  Q  N  V  P  N  G  E  I  T  F
Q  S  M  R  K  A  Q  H  P  J  R  P  V  U  O  F  N  G  U  H  X  I  B  B
Q  T  B  V  Q  J  Y  K  K  E  V  B  E  A  W  M  D  I  S  I  O  S  O  Y
C  K  W  F  X  T  S  E  N  S  I  S  B  Z  A  I  H  R  J  A  M  W  D  E
J  F  P  S  W  S  J  O  T  U  T  M  P  S  R  N  B  N  N  O  R  A  Y  B
T  B  T  E  Y  X  K  X  W  I  R  O  Q  E  M  V  Z  O  K  X  O  C  L  E
I  E  E  U  J  U  T  A  O  U  U  N  C  N  L  O  V  I  J  R  Q  E  A  N
F  U  C  C  K  A  D  N  S  Q  H  T  E  X  B  F  J  T  C  B  I  B  N  D
I  F  I  L  A  E  S  Z  O  Q  I  X  A  S  H  Z  F  A  L  C  L  G  G  Z
V  R  O  A  P  A  K  A  E  O  A  T  T  K  V  U  C  D  O  E  I  I  U  N
F  K  V  B  E  O  G  D  N  K  W  X  U  U  O  C  T  I  L  Y  S  P  A  E
R  W  F  R  Z  D  F  S  W  D  U  O  M  O  B  T  Y  L  H  M  T  Q  G  J
L  P  O  E  F  V  I  X  N  A  I  C  A  C  R  F  G  A  O  G  E  U  E  O
Y  R  E  V  A  G  I  T  G  Z  P  B  U  G  G  Q  V  V  H  P  N  R  O  E
R  B  N  N  X  R  A  Q  P  J  N  B  W  V  I  E  M  Z  S  Z  I  D  Z  G
R  K  O  O  S  Y  U  M  L  R  K  G  N  H  Z  R  I  U  B  D  N  S  U  P
P  V  T  N  T  D  L  O  B  W  D  L  W  X  J  M  Z  W  G  W  G  V  X  B
I  X  O  O  S  N  O  I  S  S  E  R  P  X  E  L  A  I  C  A  F  Z  F  S
```

Nonverbal cues	Giving directions	Asking questions
Listening	Validation	Speaking
Tone of voice	Facial expressions	Body language

Activity 6: Multiple Choice

Circle the letter beside the correct answer.

1. Alzheimer's disease is a form of:
   A. Cancer.
   B. Dementia.
   C. Osteoporosis.
   D. Cerebral palsy.

2. How can you prevent a resident who has dementia from becoming agitated?
   A. Confine the resident to their room.
   B. Provide a quiet, controlled environment.
   C. Repeatedly tell the resident to stay calm.
   D. Provide lots of exciting large group activities.

3. Mrs. Dodson says everyone wants to steal her things. This suggests she is:
   A. Delusional.
   B. Short of breath.
   C. Hard of hearing.
   D. Just teasing the staff.

4. One of your responsibilities in caring for residents with dementia is to:
   A. Anticipate their basic needs.
   B. Give them presents on holidays.
   C. Hide them from family members.
   D. Prevent them from taking too much of your time.

5. Mr. Smith tells you he has to go to work today. Using the technique called validation therapy, how would you respond to his demand to go to work?
   A. Tell him that he is too old and sick to work.
   B. Ignore his continued requests for your attention.
   C. Tell him today is a holiday and he doesn't have to work.
   D. Remind him that he is retired and has Alzheimer's disease.

Activity 7: Fill in the Blank

Complete each sentence using the correct term.

Agenda behavior   Agitation   Alzheimer's disease
Anxiety   Behavioral symptoms Cognitive impairment
Delusion   Dementia   Hallucination
Insomnia   Multi-infarct   Sundown syndrome
Wandering

1. A false thought that is thought to be real is called a(n) _____.

2. _____ is a progressive, incurable disease that affects the brain and causes memory loss and eventual death.

3. When a resident tends to follow a certain agenda, often a past routine, their behavior is referred to as _____.

4. A resident's movements that are irregular, rapid, violent, or excited and often troubled suggest the resident is experiencing _____.

5. Actions that are caused by a disease or condition are known as _____.

6. When a person moves from one place to another aimlessly, they are _____.

7. _____ is a situation later in the day when a resident may become irritable or combative, or tearful and withdrawn.

8. When a person cannot sleep enough, they have _____.

9. _____ means that a person is experiencing a disruption in knowledge, memory, awareness, or judgment.

10. The term _____ refers to a loss of mental functions such as memory, thinking, and reasoning.

11. A person is having a(n) _____ when they see or hear things that are not really there.

12. _____ is a state of uneasiness in the mind.

13. _____ - _____ is a type of damage to blood vessels that may cause a loss of function in a tissue or organ, such as the brain.

Activity 8: Matching

Match each behavioral term with the example of that behavior and an approach to care.

1. _____ Mr. Alvin doesn't do crossword puzzles anymore and always seems sad and tired. You encourage him to talk about how he feels.

2. _____ Mr. Hendricks taps his foot on the floor repeatedly. You make sure there is no physical problem causing his distress.

3. _____ Mrs. Penrose has an increased pulse rate and appears tense. You assure her that she is safe.

4. _____ Mrs. Rushman never sleeps more than two hours a night. You help her to eat properly and rest during the day.

5. _____ Mrs. Wiley believes that her family wants to hurt her. You help her feel loved and supported, without arguing about her beliefs.

6. _____ Mr. Randall sometimes has conversations with people who are not there. You listen to him without questioning who he is talking to.

7. _____ Mr. Williamson walks up and down the hallway, opening and closing doors. You help him get routine exercise.

A. Agitation

B. Anxiety

C. Delusions

D. Depression

E. Hallucinations

F. Insomnia

G. Wandering

Activity 9: Content Review

For each activity of daily living listed below, write two guidelines you can use to assist a resident who has dementia. Refer to your textbook as needed to complete this exercise.

Toileting

1. _____

2. _____

Hydration

1. _____

2. _____

Eating

1. _____

2. _____

Dressing

1. _____

2. _____

Bathing

1. _____

2. _____

Grooming

1. _____

2. _____

Activity 10: Matching

Match the term to the definition.

Term	Definition
1. _____ Nasal cannula	A. Moist warm application.
2. _____ Sitz bath	B. A bath in a tub or special basin in which only the perineum and buttocks are immersed.
3. _____ Oxygen	C. An odorless, tasteless, and colorless gas.
4. _____ Moist heat	D. A device that measures and shows how deeply a person breathes, seeing the result helps to encourage deep breathing.
5. _____ Oropharyngeal tube	E. Two-pronged tube inserted into the nostrils to deliver oxygen.
6. _____ Endotracheal tube	F. A tube placed through the mouth into the pharynx for breathing.
7. _____ Incentive spirometer	G. Blood sugar level that is too low.
8. _____ Moist cold	H. Process used for removing waste and fluid from the blood through a surgically placed catheter in the abdominal (peritoneal) cavity.
9. _____ Hypoglycemia	I. Tube placed through the mouth or nose into the trachea.
10. _____ Tracheostomy tube	J. Tube that enters the person's respiratory system.
11. _____ Peritoneal dialysis	K. A stoma through the trachea into the respiratory airway.
12. _____ Mechanical ventilator	L. A state in which the blood oxygen level shows that the body is not getting enough oxygen.
13. _____ Tracheostomy	M. Moist cold application.
14. _____ Hypoxia	N. A machine used to assist or replace spontaneous breathing when a person cannot breathe on their own.

Activity 11: Content Review

Stages of Alzheimer's Disease

List the three stages of Alzheimer's disease and provide three signs for each stage.

1. _____

Signs: _____

_____

_____

2. _____

Signs: _____

_____

_____

3. _____

Signs: _____

_____

_____

Comfort Care and End of Life
Activity 1: True or False

Beside each statement, write T for TRUE or F for FALSE.

1. _____ Untreated pain can cause a decline in a resident's health.

2. _____ A nurse assistant has an important role in helping a resident who has pain.

3. _____ Most types of pain are a normal part of aging.

4. _____ If a resident can smile, they are not in pain.

5. _____ Unmanaged pain can cause a person to feel depressed, anxious, and fearful.

6. _____ Pain medications are the only treatment options for pain management.

7. _____ Guided imagery can be used in pain management.

8. _____ Unpleasant odors can prevent a resident from sleeping.

9. _____ Pain is the fifth vital sign.

10. _____ Residents have a right to have their pain treated.

AHCA

Activity 2: Matching

Match the misconception about pain with the fact.

Misconception

1. _____ It is better not to take pain medicine until the pain is really bad.

2. _____ It is easier to deal with pain than the side effects of pain medication.

3. _____ If a resident takes too much pain medication, they will become addicted.

4. _____ Pain is a normal part of aging.

5. _____ If pain medicine no longer works for a resident, they must be addicted or immune to it.

6. _____ Nurses and nurse assistants are too busy to be bothered about a resident's pain.

Fact

A. People can develop a tolerance to medication. It does not mean they are addicted or immune. They just need a stronger dose or a new medication.

B. The risk of addiction is rare when the medication is taken for pain.

C. If you wait too long to take pain medicine, you may need a higher dose or stronger medicine. Taking medicine regularly can help manage pain.

D. Pain happens more frequently for older people, but it is not normal and should be treated.

E. It is important to treat pain. The nursing staff wants to help a resident who is in pain.

F. Pain medicines can cause side effects, but the side effects are treatable. Worries about side effects should not stop someone from taking pain medicine.

Activity 3: Spell It Out

Using the definitions and the clues provided, finish spelling out each word.

Acupuncture   Endorphins   Pain
Distraction   Guided imagery

1. These are natural morphine-like substances released by the brain during exercise, which can alter pain sensation:

    ____ ____ D____ ____ ____ ____ ____ N____

2. A bodily sensation that causes suffering and distress: ____ ____ ____ N

3. This technique is used to direct a person's attention away from their pain or discomfort:

    ____ ____ ____ T____ ____ ____ ____ ____ ____ N

4. This is a medical therapy that originated in ancient China:

    ____C____ ____ ____ ____ ____T____ ____ ____

5. Relaxation can be achieved through this technique involving words and music:

    ____U____ ____ ____ ____   I ____ ____ ____ ____R____

Activity 4: Multiple Choice

Circle the letter beside the correct answer.

1. What is the nurse assistant's role in helping residents who are in pain?
   A. To always offer the resident a hot compress for their pain.
   B. To always lead a resident through a guided imagery exercise.
   C. To always tell the charge nurse whenever a resident is in pain.
   D. To always notify the family whenever their loved one is in pain.

2. If a resident tells you their pain is a 3 on a scale of 10, what should you do?
   A. You should offer them an aspirin.
   B. You should tell the charge nurse promptly.
   C. You shouldn't do anything for so little pain.
   D. You should tell them not to worry until it is 8 or 9.

3. Untreated pain can cause a resident to feel:
   A. Sleepy.
   B. Hungry.
   C. Healthy.
   D. Hopeless.

4. A sitz bath is a type of:
   A. Dry cold.
   B. Moist heat.
   C. Acupuncture.
   D. Guided imagery.

5. What is a common side effect of pain medication?
   A. Swelling
   B. Itchy skin
   C. Incontinence
   D. Constipation

Activity 5: Matching

Nondrug Therapy

Match the letter of the correct description to the nondrug therapy.

Nondrug therapy	Description
1. _____ Acupuncture	A. A technique that uses words and sometimes music to achieve a relaxed and focused state.
2. _____ Animals	B. Strategies to reduce anxiety, muscle tension, and pain that include meditation and deep breathing.
3. _____ Distraction	C. Laughter is used as a form of distraction.
4. _____ Guided imagery	D. Pet therapy programs provide relaxation and companionship as a form of distraction.
5. _____ Heat/cold application	E. A form of electrical massage applied to specific areas of the body.
6. _____ Humor	F. A healing method in which fine needles are inserted in the body at certain sites.
7. _____ Massage	G. This application is used in various dry or moist forms to relieve pain or increase comfort.
8. _____ Relaxation	H. A form of relaxation that involves the use of slow rhythmic strokes on specific areas of the body.
9. _____ Vibration	I. Technique in which the goal is to focus the resident's attention on something other than their pain.

Activity 6: Situation and Response

Match each situation with the action a nurse assistant should take.

Situation

1. _____ The charge nurse has applied a hot pack to a resident's hip to relieve pain.

2. _____ You notice Mrs. Carlton is rubbing her shoulder and grimacing. You ask her if she is in pain and she says "No."

3. _____ You notice that a resident seems to be in pain. You ask her about it, but she says she doesn't want to bother the nurse for medication.

4. _____ You notice that a resident who is on pain medication has not had a bowel movement in two days.

5. _____ Mr. Acton has been on pain medication for three days. He has begun to sleep for several hours in the afternoon.

Response

A. Let the charge nurse know. It may be necessary for the resident to receive a laxative or stool softener.

B. Assure her that the nurse wants to know whenever a resident is in pain. Tell the charge nurse about the resident's pain.

C. Tell the charge nurse what you've observed and what the resident told you.

D. Tell the charge nurse what you've noticed. Extra sleep may be a sign of over-medication.

E. Follow the charge nurse's instructions. Check with the resident every 5 to 10 minutes. Check the site for signs of redness.

Activity 7: Situation and Response

What would you do?

Read each situation. Write the letter of the appropriate response in the space provided.

Situation

1. _____ Mrs. Littleton's roommate is very close to death. Mrs. Littleton seems agitated and upset, but doesn't seem willing to talk about her feelings.

2. _____ Mrs. Jackson is visiting her mother, who has been lingering close to death for a week. Mrs. Jackson has lost control of her emotions and is crying uncontrollably.

3. _____ Mr. Montgomery has recently been told his lung cancer has spread to his liver and stomach. He has never seemed more cheerful. When his daughter tries to talk to him about signing an advance directive, he becomes angry and changes the subject.

4. _____ Mrs. Spencer tells you that in a previous life she was a spiritual healer for a tribe of ancient Indians. You think this is ridiculous.

5. _____ One of your favorite residents is very close to death. You have been an important person in her life for over two years, but the family is ignoring you during these final hours. Your feelings are hurt.

Response

A. Let the charge nurse know what you've observed. She may choose to talk with the resident's daughter about the stages of grief. The resident seems to be in denial.

B. Respect her beliefs about reincarnation. Listen attentively when she talks, but don't force a discussion about your viewpoint.

C. Share your feelings with a trusted co-worker or friend. Remember that this is an awkward and painful time for the family. They may not ever thank you for all you have done for their loved one. You may have to comfort yourself by remembering the nice times you shared with the resident.

D. Give her an opportunity to open up about her feelings. Say something like, "You and your roommate have been such good friends; you must be very sad right now." If she doesn't want to talk, don't try to make her do so.

E. Guide her to a private or secluded area. Offer her a tissue. Pay attention to her non-verbal communication. If she seems to want privacy, leave her alone. If she wants you to stay, begin a conversation with a statement like, "This must be very difficult for you."

Activity 8: Crossword

Advanced Directive   Bereavement   Hospice

Palliative   Postmortem   Rebirth in another form of life

Across	Down
3 Reincarnation	1 A legal document used by a resident to communicate their wishes about the care they want if they become incapacitated and cannot make decisions
4 Care focused on comfort and symptom relief rather than cure	2 A program with a specially trained interdisciplinary team that cares for a terminally ill resident expected to die within six months
5 Period of grief after a loved one dies	
6 After death	

Activity 9: True or False

Beside each statement, write T for TRUE or F for FALSE.

1. _____ Everyone believes in life after death.

2. _____ Many people fear death because they are afraid of the unknown.

3. _____ The first stage of grief is bargaining.

4. _____ We all go through the stages of grief in an orderly progression.

5. _____ Bereavement is a period of grief someone goes through after a loved one dies.

6. _____ End of life care is the same as palliative care.

7. _____ Medicare covers hospice care for people who will die within 6 months.

8. _____ By forcing them to face reality, you help a dying resident reach acceptance.

9. _____ Reflection is a communication technique that may help a resident to talk about their feelings.

10. _____ The statement "I want to see my grandson graduate college," is an example of denial.

11. _____ If a dying resident seems unhappy with everything you do, they may be in the stage of anger.

12. _____ Family members of a dying resident always lose control of their emotions.

13. _____ It's OK to gossip about a resident after they have passed away.

14. _____ Just before death, a resident's eyes may stare blankly into space, with no eye movement.

15. _____ A resident's dentures should be discarded after death.

Activity 10: Multiple Choice

Circle the letter beside the correct answer.

1. You can help a dying resident cope with their feelings by:
   A. Avoiding painful topics.
   B. Forcing them to face reality.
   C. Sharing your own views about death.
   D. Listening to anything they have to say.

2. What is an advance directive?
   A. A last will and testament that is signed before the age of 50.
   B. A signed document which outlines a person's plan for reincarnation.
   C. A legal document stating the person's wishes about lifesaving care or death.
   D. A legal document stating what is to be done with your belongings after your death.

3. When a dying resident voices their anger, what should you say?
   A. "You shouldn't feel that way."
   B. "Everybody goes through this stage."
   C. "What you're going through is really hard, isn't it?"
   D. "Would you please try not to take your anger out on me?"

4. You can help the family of a dying resident by:
   A. Insisting that they pray with you.
   B. Telling them jokes or amusing stories.
   C. Helping them to laugh about their troubles.
   D. Being available to listen when they want to talk.

5. When a resident wants to talk about their funeral arrangements, it usually means they've reached the stage of:
   A. Resolution.
   B. Bargaining.
   C. Depression.
   D. Acceptance.

Ethics, Law, and Regulatory Guidelines

Activity 1: Word Search

```
W B S R B Y N M M Z P G I F T H K N U E G H H U
R I I F L Y E V R U S J Q E C I H F Z O V I Q S
A G I L N I E H U V W T S G K F P N J A A T P X
K S R O Y E V R U S P C T J E J U X R T C I B Z
W A Z W Z F T R F R C A H L V C C N Q N K F T C
X J B M E R C E D P F E G F Q U N Y G L E Z H O
I A Y L R Y N Y E S Y C I C T X H A H S Z E P I
O J N J N X X E F P K I R U O D H G V G T X T M
C S X V P K U R I G J T N J A L K Y K E T O Y F
B U R Q G E F X C J R S M R I E S U B A I U L W
I D Q W S L U E I R L U Q B X A W L C L F R Q E
H O F P O A D H E O H J U P K O A B I A G K G I
L M R L Q S B J N A G R U P Y L T G N O D J X V
Z B G R Z U O Q C R U E I G I Q V T L G Y F P R
U U H C M M N K I K L D R E S T R A I N T S F E
M D T X R T F F E D X L I F I N A L R E P O R T
Q S Z A W S L E S Q Z E G L N E G L E C T V W N
S M H P C A H T F Q O X H S N C E K M D O J F I
I A C N N F Q H T S K R X B Y X H B B G R C V F
D N B W E Q I I D U C C O D E O F C O N D U C T
J E E P T Y E C A U N I P B P H M H L V R I W B
E B M K O U K S J A T S X G O S F R N Z O N A I
T M K W E E T A N F N V V Y O F Y I I J Z M W O G
W G H F M Z R P L K Q Z J X H N D S T W V T N V
```

Final report	Surveyor	Interview
Deficiencies	Survey	Code of Conduct
Ethics	Harm	

Activity 2: Multiple Choice

What does the survey cover?

Circle the letter beside the correct answer.

1. The initial tour is designed to:
   A. Make an initial review of the facility, residents, and environment
   B. Make a determination to grant the facility another license to admit residents
   C. To go over quality data with rest of the staff
   D. Deliver the plan of correction to the charge nurses

2. Which is an example of emotional or behavioral reactions?
   A. Edema
   B. Poor oral care
   C. Resident yelling
   D. Weight loss

3. Which is an example of an environmental/safety concern for surveyors?
   A. Hand hygiene
   B. Pulling the curtain for privacy
   C. Availability of scheduled activities
   D. Resident choices for bath times

4. Which is an example of a question that could be asked of staff?
   A. Do you have privacy when speaking on the phone?
   B. Is the food served the way that you like it?
   C. What would you do if you witnessed abuse?
   D. Do you get to choose what you want to wear?

5. What is an example of a question that could be asked of a resident or family member?
   A. What would you do in case of a fire?
   B. How do you know if someone is on isolation precautions?
   C. How do people act toward you when they are giving you care?
   D. How do you know the facility policies?

Activity 3: Fill in the Blank
The Survey

Complete each sentence using the correct term.

Exit conference   Long term care survey
Initial   Quality measures
Life Safety Code

1. Safety standards for a facility are listed in the _____ _____

   _____.

2. Surveyors review the facility's history and _____ _____ documents
   before coming to the facility.

3. During the _____ stage, surveyors explain their reason for being there and any complaints that
   they will be reviewing.

4. Required for every facility that accepts Medicaid or Medicare payments _____
   _____ _____ _____.

5. The final conference with the administrator and the surveyors is called the _____

   _____.

Activity 4: Ideas to Consider

Write the answers in the space provided. Refer to the textbook if necessary.

1. Name four sources of information that are reviewed during a survey.
   A. _____
   B. _____
   C. _____
   D. _____

2. Name three different reasons for a survey and explain each.
   A. _____
   _____
   B. _____
   _____
   C. _____
   _____

3. Give examples of four quality of life issues that surveyors will be observing.
   A. _____
   B. _____
   C. _____
   D. _____

4. Give examples of at least five care areas that surveyors will consider upon their visit.
   A. _____
   B. _____
   C. _____
   D. _____
   E. _____

5. What are examples of three things that you can do during a survey to fulfill your role?
   A. _____
   B. _____
   C. _____

This page intentionally left blank.

How To Be a Nurse Assistant: Practice Exam 1

Circle the letter beside the best answer.

1. Which of these services is usually provided in a long term care facility?
   A. Home health care.
   B. Radiation therapy.
   C. Rehabilitative care.
   D. Surgery.

2. What is an example of mindful caregiving?
   A. Being on time for work.
   B. Choosing the resident's meal for them.
   C. Encouraging the resident to pick out clothing they would like to wear.
   D. Requiring a resident to stick with the facility's schedule.

3. What is an effective way to get to know a resident?
   A. Discuss the resident with housekeeping staff.
   B. Read the resident's mail and personal papers.
   C. Ask the resident about their needs and preferences.
   D. Check with the resident's roommate for information.

4. Which of these is an example of neglect?
   A. Teasing a resident in an unkind manner.
   B. Threatening a resident with physical harm.
   C. Locking a resident in their room against their will.
   D. Not taking a resident to the bathroom when they ask.

5. Which of these statements about our perceptions is true?
   A. Our perceptions about residents are always accurate.
   B. We should always believe that what we perceive is true, regardless of whether it may be right or wrong.
   C. Our perceptions influence how we behave toward others.
   D. Single-minded perceptions of residents help us get to know them better.

6. How can you make a new resident feel that they belong?
   A. Call them by the nickname "honey."
   B. Encourage them to participate in activities.
   C. Ask if you can borrow some of their jewelry.
   D. Leave them alone to adjust to the facility on their own.

7. Which of the following symptoms is typical of mid-stage dementia?
   A. Loss of appetite.
   B. Tendency to feel cold most of the time.
   C. Great difficulty making decisions.
   D. Improved recent memory.

8. Which of these nonverbal behaviors helps develop a positive relationship with a resident?
   A. Smiling warmly.
   B. Always keeping your facial expressions neutral.
   C. Looking over the resident's shoulder when you speak to them.
   D. Folding your arms across your chest.

9. What is the purpose of a living will?
   A. To settle property and financial issues when a person dies.
   B. To help family members decide how they want their loved one cared for.
   C. To keep family members away from a dying resident.
   D. To guide decisions about a person's care if they become incapacitated.

10. You're involved in an argument with a co-worker. In order to resolve the conflict, you should:
    A. Tell the co-worker what's wrong with their point of view.
    B. Bring up past conflicts you've had with the co-worker.
    C. Take time to understand the other person's point of view.
    D. Calm things down by joking about their point of view.

11. A resident's care plan is used as a tool to:
    A. Determine whether the resident qualifies for Medicaid payments.
    B. Invite family members to facility parties.
    C. Plan for new building improvements.
    D. Coordinate all treatments and services for the resident.

12. **How residents perceive and respond to pain is influenced by:**
    A. Their nutritional status.
    B. Sunlight.
    C. The clothing they are wearing at the time.
    D. Their cultural or religious background and beliefs.

13. **Whenever you prepare to do a task, you should ask yourself a number of questions, including which of the following?**
    A. Is this task in my job description?
    B. Did I get the resident's permission to do the task?
    C. Should I call the resident's family to check whether they want me to do this task?
    D. Will the charge nurse respect me more for doing this task?

14. **You can help to break the chain of infection at each link by:**
    A. Sterilizing all bed linen every morning.
    B. Disinfecting all surfaces.
    C. Wearing a gown and protective eyewear at all times.
    D. Performing hand hygiene before and after every contact with a resident.

15. **When a family member is angry or critical, you should:**
    A. Take their comments personally.
    B. Explain that the facility is understaffed and there's nothing anyone can do.
    C. Be supportive and report the situation to the charge nurse.
    D. Pretend you agree with them that the facility is not doing a good job.

16. **Your role in helping maintain a resident's nutrition includes:**
    A. Planning meals for the week.
    B. Helping food service staff prepare meals.
    C. Insisting that residents eat everything on their plate.
    D. Serving meals while hot foods are still hot and cold foods are cold.

17. **To make sure a resident is safe during a bath, you should:**
    A. Close the tub room door.
    B. Undress the resident in the tub room.
    C. Check the water temperature.
    D. Remove all your jewelry.

18. **As a nurse assistant, you typically learn about a resident's symptoms by:**
    A. Interviewing the resident's roommate.
    B. Talking to the resident.
    C. Observing the resident while they sleep.
    D. Taking the resident's vital signs.

19. **Which of the following occurs because of nervous system changes as we age?**
    A. Slowing of respirations.
    B. Slowing of heartbeat.
    C. Decreased insulin production.
    D. Decreased short-term memory.

20. **The Heimlich maneuver is used with a resident who is:**
    A. Vomiting.
    B. Having a seizure.
    C. Choking.
    D. Feeling nauseous.

21. **How can you help a resident be independent?**
    A. Select their clothing for them each day.
    B. Encourage the resident to do what they can.
    C. Insist on helping them with bathing.
    D. Leave them alone to take care of themselves.

22. **The Resident's Bill of Rights includes:**
    A. The right to have a private room.
    B. The right to be happy all the time.
    C. The right to privacy and confidentiality.
    D. The right to receive all services free of charge.

23. **The nurse asks you to give ROM exercise to a resident who is confined to bed. According to her care plan, there are no restrictions. What does "no restrictions" mean?**
    A. You should work their joints and muscles very hard.
    B. Provide ROM exercise as often as possible on each shift.
    C. The resident should be able to do all of the exercises alone.
    D. You may move each joint through its full available range.

24. **Mr. Nathanson is experiencing a seizure and you have called for help. What else should you do for him?**
    A. Pour water into his mouth.
    B. Help him to the floor to prevent a fall.
    C. Put a toothbrush or something firm between his teeth for him to bite on.
    D. Ask other residents to help you hold him down firmly.

25. **When you maintain the resident's privacy during all aspects of personal care, which theme of care are you paying attention to?**
   A. Respect.
   B. Safety.
   C. Communication.
   D. Infection control.

26. **Using good body mechanics will help you:**
   A. Get all your work done before your shift ends.
   B. Lose weight.
   C. Avoid injuries.
   D. Develop stronger muscles.

27. **You should check a resident's vital signs:**
   A. Only on the first day of each month.
   B. Whenever a change occurs that might signal an illness or as assigned by the charge nurse.
   C. Everyday at the beginning of your shift.
   D. Whenever you feel like it.

28. **If a resident starts to feel dizzy as you help them stand up from their bed to get to their walker, you should:**
   A. Move them quickly to the walker before they have a chance to fall.
   B. Help them to lie down in bed and call for the charge nurse.
   C. Keep them standing for a minute until the dizziness passes.
   D. Have them sit on the edge of the bed while you go to talk to the charge nurse.

29. **Your role in the care plan meeting includes:**
   A. Sharing information about the resident.
   B. Serving coffee and doughnuts to the interdisciplinary team.
   C. Deciding which doctors and nurses should attend.
   D. Diagnosing the resident's medical condition.

30. **When you position a resident on their side, their legs should normally be positioned:**
   A. With a pillow between them.
   B. However you think.
   C. With both legs straight and slightly apart.
   D. With both legs bent at 90°.

31. **When you provide personal care, it is important to:**
   A. Have all morning care done before 8 a.m.
   B. Never give care that has not been clearly requested by the family.
   C. Keep on schedule, even if you have to rush slow residents.
   D. Encourage the resident to do all that they can for themselves.

32. **How can you help a family get over their guilt when a resident is admitted into a long-term care facility?**
   A. Encourage them to question their decision to admit their family member.
   B. Give their family member the best care you can.
   C. Tell them they are in charge of bathing and dressing their family member whenever they visit.
   D. Just nod and smile whenever they make suggestions about their loved one's care.

33. **What is a common cause of a pressure injury?**
   A. Uncomfortable clothing.
   B. Dirty pajamas.
   C. Pressure on the skin.
   D. Stress caused by family arguments.

34. **What is a benefit of observing residents carefully while providing personal care?**
   A. It frees you from having to observe residents at other times.
   B. You have the opportunity to talk with residents about family members.
   C. You may note both physical and psychological changes in residents.
   D. You can decide whether or not to give residents their medications, depending on how they feel.

35. **Why is it important to make a neat, wrinkle free bed?**
   A. Wrinkles give germs places to grow.
   B. It is more difficult to launder sheets that become very wrinkled.
   C. Wrinkled sheets can cause skin irritation and breakdown.
   D. Old-fashioned charge nurses think neat beds look better.

36. **The signs and symptoms of dehydration may include:**
   A. Blurred vision.
   B. Rosy pink skin color.
   C. Decreased urine output.
   D. Elevated blood pressure.

37. **Why is it important to be familiar with a resident's elimination pattern?**
    A. So that you never have to clean up an accident.
    B. So that you can recognize and report any changes.
    C. To keep the family informed at every visit.
    D. Because you discuss every resident's elimination at the end of your shift.

38. **Why is it good practice to use a gait belt when transferring a resident?**
    A. You never need other helpers.
    B. It helps to support the resident's body during the transfer.
    C. It keeps the resident's clothing in place during the transfer.
    D. It makes the transfer go twice as fast.

39. **You are a new nurse assistant at your facility. How might you learn that a certain resident has frequent incontinence?**
    A. By checking the resident's medical record.
    B. By interviewing all family members that come to visit the resident.
    C. By sneaking into the resident's room at lunch to check the sheets for dampness.
    D. By asking the laundry to check the resident's clothing for urine stains.

40. **When you give ROM exercises, it is important to:**
    A. Wear gloves and a gown.
    B. Exercise the resident at least until they begin to sweat.
    C. Follow the therapist's written plan.
    D. Move each joint just to the point where it begins to be painful.

41. **What is an ICF?**
    A. A facility that provides nursing and supportive care to residents who have a variety of mental or physical disabilities.
    B. A specialized facility that provides care for an elderly disabled person.
    C. A congregate care facility for elderly residents with diabetes.
    D. A facility that provides a home-like environment for people in wheelchairs.

42. **A resident's daughter complains to you that you ask her mother to bathe herself. How should you answer the daughter?**
    A. You have a lot of people to care for and don't have time for everyone.
    B. You suggest the daughter care for the mother herself.
    C. You ask the daughter file a formal complaint.
    D. You explain you are helping her mother maintain her independence.

43. **You are communicating assertively when you:**
    A. Feel guilty after saying you cannot volunteer for an extra shift.
    B. Share your complaints with residents.
    C. Speak up for yourself without hurting others.
    D. Say what you think other people will want to hear.

44. **To prevent a stage one pressure injury from getting worse, you should:**
    A. Frequently give the resident ice chips to suck on.
    B. Give the resident three vitamin pills daily.
    C. Follow the charge nurse's instructions.
    D. Cover the area with a warm, moist cloth at all times.

45. **When a resident with an infection is on contact precautions, you should:**
    A. Never allow any visitors under any circumstances.
    B. Request that the charge nurse provide all care.
    C. Wear gloves and a gown when providing care.
    D. Install a special air ventilation system.

46. **Which of the following techniques is helpful when you are dealing with an agitated resident?**
    A. Yelling.
    B. Distraction.
    C. Reality orientation.
    D. Clapping your hands and stomping your foot.

47. **Which of the following is a developmentally disabled person?**
    A. A person who lost use of their legs after a car accident.
    B. A person with Down syndrome.
    C. A person with a chronic, severe physical disability that developed in childhood.
    D. A frail elderly person who needs assistance with bathing and dressing.

48. You can help a dying resident cope with their feelings by:
    A. Discouraging them from talking about painful topics.
    B. Using techniques of reality orientation.
    C. Explaining your own views about death.
    D. Listening to what they have to say.

49. After you make rounds, you prioritize your tasks based on:
    A. Which tasks require the most supplies.
    B. Which tasks can be completed most quickly.
    C. What tasks you'll have to leave for the next shift.
    D. The residents' needs.

50. How can you demonstrate your desire to be a good employee?
    A. Be late to work no more than once a week.
    B. Record care activities in the resident's medical record even before you have done them.
    C. Cooperate with other team members.
    D. Offer to share your lunch with other nurse assistants.

51. You should limit your daily intake of carbohydrates to one serving of meat, poultry, fish, dry beans, or nuts. One serving means
    A. 2-3 ounces of cooked lean meat.
    B. 1 lb of cooked dry beans.
    C. four eggs.
    D. 3 tablespoons of peanut butter.

52. What is "mindful caregiving"?
    A. Wearing comfortable shoes and clothing to work.
    B. Storing soiled equipment and supplies in the clean supply room.
    C. Paying attention to details and being open, observant, and flexible.
    D. Sharing your opinions about a resident's care with their family members.

53. Aging changes happen to everyone. Which of these changes is a normal part of aging?
    A. The need to be fed.
    B. An inability to walk.
    C. Thinning of the skin.
    D. The loss of one's teeth.

54. Walkers, canes, and crutches are examples of which type of device?
    A. Orthotic.
    B. Assistive.
    C. Listening.
    D. Prosthetic.

55. When caring for a resident you must consider:
    A. Your own schedule.
    B. Your own preferences.
    C. The resident's preferences.
    D. The housekeeping schedule.

56. A history of a resident includes both

    _____ , _____

    and _____ information.

57. A physical exam proceeds through each _____

    _____.

58. A program with a specially trained interdisciplinary team that cares for a terminally ill resident who is expected to die within 6 months is called

    _____.

59. Blood sugar is lowered by the person receiving

    _____.

60. Oxygen is used to treat or prevent symptoms of:

    _____

    _____.

This page intentionally left blank.

How To Be a Nurse Assistant: Practice Exam 2

Circle the letter beside the best answer.

1. Long term care is a growing area of the health care industry. Why do you think that is true?
   A. Long term care is required by law.
   B. People enjoy living in long term care.
   C. There is an increasing elderly population.
   D. People prefer long term care to living alone.

2. Nursing home is a term commonly used for long term care facilities. What other name is used?
   A. Fitness center.
   B. Dialysis center.
   C. Intensive care unit.
   D. Rehabilitation center.

3. Why do people enter long term care facilities?
   A. For a long vacation.
   B. To get away from family.
   C. To participate in bingo games.
   D. For assistance with personal care.

4. What services does nursing staff provide?
   A. Help with ADL's, medical treatments, medications and health promotion.
   B. Speech pathology.
   C. Admission services.
   D. Building maintenance.

5. When caring for a resident, what is the most important thing to consider?
   A. Your own schedule.
   B. Your own preferences.
   C. The resident's preferences.
   D. The housekeeping schedule.

6. What is resident-centered care?
   A. Using your mind to the best of your abilities.
   B. Knowing everything about the nervous system.
   C. Focusing on the resident's preferences and needs with the resident being an active participant in their care.
   D. Giving care the way a resident's roommate thinks is best.

7. Being a good employee means:
   A. Being pretty.
   B. Being reliable.
   C. Being passive.
   D. Being aggressive.

8. Pivot discs are used to help a resident:
   A. Exercise
   B. Use a walker.
   C. Transfer from the bed to chair.
   D. Perform range-of-motion exercises.

9. When should you review your facility's disaster plan?
   A. After a disaster.
   B. In your free time.
   C. Soon after you are hired.
   D. During an actual disaster.

10. Which of these safety rules can you follow to prevent slips and falls?
    A. Be on time.
    B. Walk really fast.
    C. Wear nonskid shoes.
    D. Rush residents along.

11. What should you do to increase the safety of residents?
    A. Use proper body mechanics.
    B. Never reach overhead for something.
    C. Use quick or jerky movements.
    D. Encourage the resident to use hand rails.

12. The phrase "body mechanics" is defined as:
    A. Injury prevention.
    B. A pivot stand transfer.
    C. Using your body efficiently.
    D. Using a mechanical lift correctly.

13. Good health comes from a combination of factors. Which of the following is one of those?
    A. Smoking.
    B. Overeating.
    C. Good nutrition.
    D. Lack of exercise.

14. Managing stress is important because:
    A. The charge nurse believes it is important.
    B. People can tell when you are having a bad day.
    C. Prolonged stress might cause you to become ill.
    D. You might lose your job if you show any stress.

15. **Which of these statements about residents' spiritual needs is true?**
    A. Nurse assistants should never discuss religion with residents.
    B. Like all people, residents express their spirituality in different ways.
    C. If a resident doesn't talk about religion they must not believe in God.
    D. Only family members and clergy can help residents meet their spiritual needs.

16. **Which of the following is considered a need on Maslow's hierarchy?**
    A. Wealth.
    B. Physical well-being.
    C. New clothing.
    D. Annual vacations.

17. **A resident is being visited by their spouse, and they want privacy. You should:**
    A. Leave the door to the room open.
    B. Respect their desire to be alone together.
    C. Tell them they are not allowed to have sex.
    D. Report this information to the charge nurse.

18. **What is the correct view of residents' rights?**
    A. Rights are decided by the charge nurse.
    B. Rights don't always need to be honored.
    C. Rights are each person's legal protection.
    D. Rights are things residents complain about.

19. **How can you protect a resident's right to privacy?**
    A. Only discuss a resident's problems with your sister.
    B. Only discuss a resident's problems with a good friend.
    C. Only discuss a resident's problems with their roommate.
    D. Only discuss a resident's problems with the charge nurse.

20. **The heart, veins, and arteries are part of which system?**
    A. Urinary.
    B. Sensory.
    C. Circulatory.
    D. Reproductive.

21. **Aging changes happen to everyone. Which of these changes is also a normal part of aging?**
    A. The need to be fed.
    B. An inability to walk.
    C. Loss of muscle mass.
    D. The loss of all of one's teeth.

22. **When you notice a change in a resident, what should you do?**
    A. Report the change to housekeeping.
    B. Wait to see if the change gets worse.
    C. Report the change to the charge nurse.
    D. Call the resident's doctor immediately.

23. **In long term care, a sign is:**
    A. Something you can observe.
    B. Something you hope will happen.
    C. Something the resident tells you about.
    D. Something you think may be happening.

24. **The hair, fingernails, and mucous membranes are considered extensions of which system?**
    A. Nervous.
    B. Respiratory.
    C. Reproductive.
    D. Integumentary.

25. **A resident's significant others are defined as:**
    A. A husband or wife.
    B. Brothers and sisters.
    C. The immediate family only.
    D. Anyone important to the resident.

26. **When a loved one is admitted to a facility, the family is likely to feel:**
    A. Dizzy.
    B. Happy.
    C. Excited.
    D. Uncertain.

27. **Which of the following statements is NOT a good way to end a conversation with a resident?**
    A. "I have 10 minutes before I have to do something else."
    B. "You're not the only person here, so please stop rambling."
    C. "I've enjoyed our conversation. Can we continue after dinner?"
    D. "I need to check on some other residents, but I'll come back shortly."

28. **How can you make it easier for others to understand you?**
    A. Mumble your words.
    B. Speak clearly and slowly.
    C. Hold your hands over your mouth.
    D. Use your hands to gesture as you talk.

29. **Nonverbal communication includes:**
    A. Singing.
    B. Yelling.
    C. Talking.
    D. Nodding.

30. **Microorganisms are small cells that can be seen only under a microscope. Which of the following is an example of a microorganism?**
    A. Nerves.
    B. Bacteria.
    C. Intestine.
    D. Epidermis.

31. **The Occupational Safety and Health Administration is abbreviated as:**
    A. CDC.
    B. OBRA.
    C. OSHA.
    D. CMMS.

32. **The chain of transmission of infection includes:**
    A. An open door.
    B. Hand washing.
    C. Portal of entry.
    D. Nutritious foods.

33. **As a nurse assistant, you should perform hand hygiene:**
    A. No more than once per shift.
    B. While shopping for groceries.
    C. Before you talk to the charge nurse.
    D. Before and after every resident contact.

34. **Gowns, gloves, masks, aprons, and goggles are called:**
    A. The long term care uniform.
    B. The nurse assistant's uniform.
    C. Personal protection equipment.
    D. Protective gear for charge nurses.

35. **The correct hand washing procedure includes:**
    A. Using soap and water.
    B. Counting to 100 slowly.
    C. Wiping your hands on your uniform.
    D. Drying your hands by blowing on them.

36. **If you incorporate the themes of care into your work, you will be providing what kind of care?**
    A. Fast and efficient care.
    B. Mindless care in an efficient way.
    C. Quality care in a timely and efficient manner.
    D. Care in which only high priority tasks are done.

37. **One of the themes of care is:**
    A. Quality control.
    B. Infection control.
    C. Telecommunications.
    D. Continuing education.

38. **The nursing team includes:**
    A. The physical therapist.
    B. The director of nursing.
    C. The activities coordinator.
    D. The occupational therapist.

39. **If you were gathering information about a resident, where would you start first?**
    A. The resident.
    B. The physician.
    C. The housekeeper.
    D. The social worker.

40. **A resident tells you they are having chest pain. When should you report this information?**
    A. Routinely.
    B. Immediately.
    C. By a certain time.
    D. When you have the time.

41. **What is the goal of rehabilitative services?**
    A. To help residents get to activities without assistance from staff.
    B. To help all residents learn to walk without assistance from staff.
    C. To enable all residents to do personal care activities by themselves.
    D. To help residents regain or maintain their level of independent functioning.

42. **Which of these devices is a prosthesis?**
    A. A brace.
    B. A wheelchair.
    C. An artificial eye.
    D. A 4-pronged cane.

43. **Braces are examples of which type of device?**
    A. Assistive.
    B. Orthotic.
    C. Listening.
    D. Prosthetic.

44. **Why is it important for a resident to have short- and long-term goals for rehabilitation?**
   A. So that the nurse assistant always has something to do.
   B. Short- and long-term goals help to keep a resident busy.
   C. So that the resident always has something to look forward to.
   D. Short- and long-term goals establish a direction and a plan of care.

45. **When caring for a resident who has Alzheimer's, you have a responsibility to:**
   A. Give them the correct medications.
   B. Sing nursery rhymes and play games.
   C. Discover and use the resident's abilities.
   D. Prevent the resident from getting confused.

46. **What is a symptom?**
   A. Something the charge nurse explains.
   B. A change in a resident that you observe.
   C. Objective information the doctor tells you about.
   D. A feeling or physical change the resident complains about.

47. **Which of the following signs is an indication of impending death?**
   A. Rapid eye movement.
   B. A pressure ulcer.
   C. Rapid, weak, and irregular pulse.
   D. A request to see a family member.

48. **In order to avoid injury, what factor should you consider?**
   A. The time of day.
   B. The temperature.
   C. Your own abilities.
   D. Your ability to sing.

49. **Which of these repetitive motions could cause injury?**
   A. Reading a book.
   B. Holding a large ball.
   C. Brushing your teeth twice a day.
   D. Bending down to pick something up.

50. **Sexual feelings involve:**
   A. Physical feelings only.
   B. Emotional feelings only.
   C. Feelings shared by young people only.
   D. Caring, loving feelings shared by two people.

51. **Inservice education is important because:**
   A. It prepares you for the nurse assistant exam that you have to take every year.
   B. You get paid more for every hour of inservice you take.
   C. The nurse assistants with the most hours of inservice get to pick their shifts.
   D. It gives you an opportunity to grow, change, and improve.

52. **To become or stay physically fit you should:**
   A. Exercise only if your doctor says you need to.
   B. Exercise 1 minute per pound per day that you are overweight.
   C. Exercise at least 2.5 to 5 hours a week.
   D. Exercise a minimum of an hour every day.

53. **Which of these tasks is performed by nursing staff?**
   A. Prescribing medications.
   B. Giving medications.
   C. Planning menus for the whole facility.
   D. Repairing medical equipment.

54. **How can you help a resident manage their pain?**
   A. Make the lights in their room as bright as possible.
   B. Report any signs or symptoms of pain to the charge nurse.
   C. Offer them plenty of snacks and beverages between meals.
   D. Turn the television up loud.

55. **Why is it important to wear gloves when you provide mouth care?**
   A. So you won't have to wash your hands.
   B. The resident may have a cold.
   C. In case the resident's gums bleed.
   D. In case you get toothpaste on your hands.

56. **Which food group is high in calcium, promotes bone health and can prevent the onset of osteoporosis?**
   A. Dairy
   B. Grains
   C. Vegetables
   D. Fruits

57. **A severe mental disorder that affects how a person thinks, acts and behaves.**
   A. Autism
   B. Down syndrome
   C. Bipolar disorder
   D. Schizophrenia

58. Attempting to understand a resident's feelings by entering their world is known as:
    A. Validation therapy
    B. Agenda behavior
    C. Reality orientation
    D. Providing verbal cues

59. A common mood disorder that causes persistent sadness and lack of interest in doing things:
    A. Obsessive-Compulsive disorder
    B. Depression
    C. Bipolar disorder
    D. Anxiety

60. A resident that leaks a small amount of urine when they laugh or sneeze, would have what type of incontinence?
    A. Stress incontinence
    B. Urge incontinence
    C. Bowel incontinence
    D. Functional incontinence

This page intentionally left blank.

Applying a Disposable Incontinence Brief

Does the candidate:

☐ Check the care plan

☐ Knock, introduce self, and address resident by preferred name.

☐ Perform hand hygiene

☐ Gather supplies and secures assistance if needed:

    ☐ Disposable incontinence brief

    ☐ Plastic trash bag

    ☐ Towel

    ☐ Underpants (if resident wears underpants over brief)

    ☐ Three pairs of gloves

    ☐ Two washcloths

    ☐ Soap or perineal wash

☐ Explain procedure and ask about resident preferences.

☐ Respect privacy and rights at all times.

Continue with the following steps:

Incontinence briefs are available in various types and sizes. Make sure to use the correct size for the resident.

☐ Put on gloves.

☐ Place an incontinence pad on the bed to protect clean linen.

☐ Help the resident onto their back.

☐ Help remove garments below the waist.

☐ Discard the soiled incontinence brief in the plastic trash bag.

☐ Remove and dispose of your soiled gloves and perform hand hygiene.

☐ Put on new gloves.

☐ With the resident on their side, give perineal care, including cleaning the rectal area.

☐ Remove and dispose of your soiled gloves and perform hand hygiene.

☐ Put on new gloves.

☐ Fan-fold one-half of the brief under the resident's buttocks.

☐ Help the resident move onto their back. Unfold the side that was fan-folded, and open the adhesive tabs on both sides. Place the brief upward between the resident's legs, and join the tab from the back of the brief to the tab in the front

of the brief. Make sure to have the leg openings pulled securely into the resident's groin areas and not resting on their thighs.

☐ If the resident wears underpants over the brief, put these on, and help the resident put on their clothing.

Note: If a panty liner is used instead of briefs, use the same procedure but instead, place the liner over their buttocks. Then have the resident move onto their back, and bring the front of the liner up between their legs. Put on their underpants and help with other clothing.

Finish with the following steps:

☐ Determine the resident's preferred position for comfort and ask them if they need anything else.

☐ Examine the environment for safety and cleanliness.

☐ Secure the call light and any other needed items within reach of the resident.

☐ Document the procedure and report any findings to the staff in charge.

_____ out of _____ = _____ %   Date: _____

Name: _____   Reviewer: _____

Competency Checklist

Applying and Removing PPE

There are different methods for applying and removing PPE. This procedure demonstrates one method. Review your facility policies and procedures related to when and how to use PPE.

To Apply PPE

☐ Remove jewelry.

☐ Perform hand hygiene.

☐ Put on gown:

    ☐ Gently open the gown without shaking.

    ☐ Insert your arms in the sleeves, with the opening in the back.

    ☐ Tie the gown at the neck and waist. The gown should cover your uniform from your neck to your knees.

☐ Put on mask or respirator:

    ☐ Put mask or respirator over your nose and mouth.

    ☐ Extend under your chin.

    ☐ Tie or secure the straps around the back of your head so that the mask fits tightly.

    ☐ Pinch the metal piece on the bridge of the nose to make a tight seal. If a N95 respirator is used, perform a seal check/fit-check.

☐ Put on goggles and face shield:

    ☐ If a N95 respirator is used, make sure that it does not interfere with proper position of your goggles.

☐ Put on gloves:

    ☐ Gloves should extend and cover the cuffs of the gown.

To Remove PPE

Remove the respirator after leaving the resident's room and closing the door.

The outside surface of the gloves, face shield, goggles and front and sleeves of the gown, and the front surfaces of the mask are considered contaminated. If at any time your hand become contaminated while touching the outside of these surfaces, stop and perform hand hygiene before continuing.

☐ Remove Gloves: *Use the steps shown below if you are right-handed. If you are left-handed, use the opposite hand.*

    ☐ Using your right hand, grasp the outside of the glove on the left hand at the inside of the wrist, turning the glove inside out as you pull it down over your left hand.

    ☐ Hold the used left glove in a ball in your gloved right hand.

    ☐ Grasp the inside of the right glove at the top of the wrist with your left hand.

    If you are wearing fitted, sterile gloves, you will not be able to grasp the inside of the top of the right glove, so you must cuff (fold over) the top of the right glove before you begin to remove the glove.

☐ Pull the right glove down over your right hand and over the used glove held in that hand. The right glove is now inside out, with the left glove enclosed in it.

☐ Place the gloves in the trash receptacle. Follow your facility's infection control policies to dispose of soiled waste.

☐ Remove Goggles or Face Shield

  ☐ Remove goggles or face shield from the back by lifting head band or ear pieces.

  ☐ If the item is reusable, follow facility policy on cleaning. Otherwise, discard in a waste container.

☐ Remove Gown:

  ☐ Untie the gown at your neck and waist.

  ☐ Pull the gown away from the neck and shoulders, touching the inside of the gown only. The gown can also be removed by, grasping the cuff of one of the sleeves and pull the sleeve down over that hand.

  ☐ Pull the other sleeve off with your covered hand.

  ☐ Carefully roll up the gown, keeping the soiled surface inside, making sure not to touch the outside of the gown.

  ☐ When removing a cloth gown that will be laundered, put it in the appropriate linen hamper. Place a disposable paper gown in the appropriate trash receptacle, following your facility's policy.

☐ Remove Mask or Respirator

  ☐ Remove the mask by untying the ties or pulling the straps over your ears or head. If a respirator is worn, pull the bottom strap over your head first, then pull the top strap on over your head.

  ☐ Fold the outside edges of the mask together, keeping the soiled sides together. Dispose of the mask or respirator in the trash, following your facility's policy.

☐ Perform hand hygiene.

_____ out of _____ = _____ %   Date: _____

Name: _____   Reviewer: _____

Applying Elastic Stockings

Does the candidate:

☐ Check care plan.

☐ Knock, introduce self, and address resident by preferred name.

☐ Perform hand hygiene.

☐ Gather equipment and secure assistance if needed:

    ☐ Elastic stockings of the correct size and length   ☐ Towel

    ☐ Wash basin half filled with warm water   ☐ Soap

    ☐ Washcloth

☐ Explain procedure and ask about resident preferences.

☐ Respect privacy and rights at all times.

Continue with the following steps:

It is important to use the correct size of support stockings. Stockings should be snug enough to provide support but not too tight or too loose. Check with the charge nurse if you are unsure about the stocking size. Apply the stockings in the morning before the resident moves their legs off the bed. This helps to prevent pooling of fluid in the feet.

☐ Make sure the stockings are clean and dry.

☐ Help the resident lie on their back.

☐ Expose only the person's legs.

☐ Observe the person's legs for swelling, moles, cuts, bruising, or other changes in skin color or appearance.

☐ Clean and dry the legs and feet before applying elastic stockings.

☐ Apply one elastic stocking at a time. Begin by rolling the stocking with your hands so that only the toe section is exposed. Put the stocking on the person's leg, positioning the opening over the top of the toes. Make sure the heel is properly placed. Then roll the stocking up the leg as far as it will go.

☐ Repeat the process on the other leg. The stockings should fit firmly and have no wrinkles.

☐ Check for good circulation and movement by observing the person's toes for color and ability to move freely.

☐ Make sure the resident knows not to roll the stockings down. Doing so can greatly reduce circulation in the legs.

☐ Ask the resident to call you if they become uncomfortable.

Finish with the following steps:

☐ Determine the resident's preferred position for comfort and ask them if they need anything else.

☐ Examine the environment for safety and cleanliness.

☐ Secure the call light and any other needed items within reach of the resident.

☐ Perform hand hygiene.

☐ Document the procedure and report any findings to the staff in charge.

_____ out of _____ = _____ %   Date: _____

Name: _____   Reviewer: _____

Competency Checklist

Assistance with Dressing a Dependent Resident

Does the candidate:

☐ Check the care plan.

☐ Knock, introduce self, and address resident by preferred name.

☐ Perform hand hygiene.

☐ Gather supplies and secure assistance if needed.

    ☐ Resident's clothing of choice

    ☐ Socks and shoes, if needed

    ☐ Accessories (such as a belt or jewelry)

☐ Explain the procedure and ask about resident preferences.

☐ Respect privacy and rights at all times.

Continue with the following steps:

As a general rule, if a resident has a weak or paralyzed limb, dress the weak side first. Dress the upper body first, then the lower body.

☐ Remove resident's nightgown or pajamas. For privacy and to prevent chill, remove the top portion of the resident's gown or pajamas first, starting with the unaffected side. Remove from the affected (weak) arm last.

☐ Help the resident put on an undershirt or bra, shirt or blouse, or dress. If a resident has a weak or paralyzed arm or has an IV in place, assist with putting that arm in the sleeve first. With an IV, move the solution through the sleeve first and hang it on the pole. Gently guide the resident's arm through the sleeve, being careful not to dislodge the IV needle or tubing. If the resident has an IV pump, call the nurse for assistance.

☐ Help the resident put on underwear, socks, or stockings, and pants or a skirt.

To put on a garment that opens in the back:

    ☐ Slide the sleeve onto the resident's arm on the weaker side.

    ☐ Slide the sleeve onto the arm of the stronger side.

    ☐ Bring the sides of the garment to the back.

    ☐ Turn the resident toward you, and bring one side of the garment to the back.

    ☐ Turn the resident away from you, and bring the other side of the garment to the back.

    ☐ Fasten the buttons, snaps, ties, or zipper.

    ☐ Place the resident in the supine position.

To put on a garment that opens in the front:

    ☐ Slide the sleeve onto the resident's arm on the weaker side.

    ☐ Bring the resident to a sitting position, and bring the garment around the back. Lower the resident to the supine position.

    ☐ Slide the sleeve onto the resident's arm on the stronger side.

    ☐ Fasten buttons, snaps, ties, or zipper.

To put on a pullover garment:

- ☐ Place the resident in the supine position.
- ☐ Open any zippers or other closures, and place the garment over the resident's head.
- ☐ Slide the sleeve of the garment onto the arm on the resident's weaker side.
- ☐ Raise the resident to a semi-sitting position, bring the garment down over the shoulder, and slide the sleeve of the garment down the arm on the resident's stronger side. If the resident cannot sit upright, turn him or her toward you and pull the garment down on the back. Then turn the resident on the other side, and slide the stronger arm and shoulder into the sleeve. Pull the garment down in the back.
- ☐ Fasten the buttons, snaps, ties, or zipper.

To put on pants or slacks:

- ☐ Slide each pant leg over the resident's foot and up the leg.
- ☐ Ask the resident to raise their hips and buttocks off the bed.
- ☐ Bring the pants up over the hips and buttocks. If the resident cannot raise their hips and buttocks, turn them onto their stronger side. Then pull the pants up over the hips and buttocks on the weaker side. Turn the resident onto the other side and repeat the process.
- ☐ Fasten the buttons, snaps, ties, or zipper.

- ☐ Help the resident put on socks or stocking and shoes or non-skid slippers before they stand so they do not slip on the floor. When putting shoes on a resident who is in bed, first place a pad on the bed to protect the bedding.
- ☐ Help the resident stand to you can smooth out their clothing, if possible, and smooth out their clothing, fasten any remaining closured, and neatly tuck in their shirt or blouse.
- ☐ Help them put on any accessories they want to wear.
- ☐ If a resident wears eyeglasses, dentures or a hearing aide, help the resident with these items. If a resident uses a prosthesis, check to see if it is to be put on before or after getting dressed.
- ☐ Collect soiled garments, and place them in a hamper for laundry, according to the facility's policy. Perform hand hygiene.
- ☐ If the resident is in bed, after dressing, help him or her out of bed.

Finish with the following steps:

- ☐ Determine the resident's preferred position for comfort and ask them if they need anything else.
- ☐ Examine ther environment for safety and cleanliness.
- ☐ Secure the call light and any other needed items within reach of the resident.
- ☐ Perform hand hygiene.
- ☐ Document the procedure and report any findings to the staff in charge.

_____ out of _____ = _____ %   Date: _____

Name: _____   Reviewer: _____

Competency Checklist
Assistance with Undressing a Dependent Resident

Does the candidate:

☐ Check the care plan

☐ Knock, introduce self, and address resident by preferred name.

☐ Perform hand hygiene

☐ Gather supplies and secures assistance if needed:

    ☐ Resident's choice of clothing

☐ Explain procedure and ask about resident preferences.

☐ Respect privacy and rights at all times.

Continue with the following steps:

This procedure is easier if the resident is sitting on the side of the bed. As a general rule, undress and dress the upper body first, then the lower body. If a resident has a weak or paralyzed arm or an IV, remove clothing from the other side first and then from the weak side or the side with the IV. If the resident has an IV, carefully guide the tubing and solution through the sleeve as the resident's arm moves.

☐ Help the resident remove garments from the upper body (shirt, dress, blouse, and undergarments).

☐ Help the resident put on a pajama top, t-shirt, or a nightgown.

☐ Help the resident remove their shoes and socks or stockings. Then help with removing the pants or skirt and undergarments, if those are to be removed.

☐ Help the resident put on pajama bottoms or other bottoms such as underpants, boxer shorts, or sweat pants.

☐ Help the resident into bed.

Finish with the following steps:

☐ Determine the resident's preferred position for comfort and ask them if they need anything else.

☐ Examine the environment for safety and cleanliness.

☐ Secure the call light and any other needed items within reach of the resident.

☐ Document the procedure and report any findings to the staff in charge.

_____ out of _____ = _____ %

Date: _____

Name: _____

Reviewer: _____

Competency Checklist
Assisting Residents with Meals

Candidate proceeds with the following steps:

☐ Check care plan.

☐ Knock, introduce self, and address resident by preferred name.

☐ Perform hand hygiene.

☐ Gather equipment and secure assistance if needed:

☐ Explain procedure and ask about resident preferences.

☐ Respect privacy and rights at all times.

Continue with the following steps:

☐ Prepare the resident before the meal by helping with grooming, performing hand hygiene, and oral care as needed.

☐ Help the resident to the dining room or make him/her comfortable in their own room.

☐ In the dining room, transfer the resident from a wheelchair to a dining room chair, if possible.

☐ Perform hand hygiene. This is an important part of infection control.

☐ Position napkins and clothing protectors if requested by the resident.

☐ Deliver trays as quickly as possible to keep foods at the correct temperature.

☐ When you remove the tray from the cart, first check the tray card. Confirm that you have the correct tray for the person you are serving and that the food is correct for the resident's diet. Check if there are any special feeding instructions.

☐ Remove the food from the tray, and place plates and bowls directly on the table. When the resident is ready to eat, remove any covers, liners, and wrappings and open condiments and cartons. Place covers and wrappings back on the tray and return the tray to the service cart or to another cart.

☐ Place plates and bowls within the resident's easy reach. Review the meal items with residents who may not see well or who may be unfamiliar with some foods. Describe the foods positively so the resident looks forward to eating.

☐ Once you have served the first resident at the table, move on to others at the same table. Serve all residents at a table before moving to the next table.

☐ Ask residents if they need help cutting food or if they would like seasoning (if permitted). Encourage residents to be as independent as possible, but watch for those who need help. Cut food into small pieces to prevent choking.

☐ Check with residents often to offer help as needed or to encourage them to eat.

☐ Give all residents enough time to finish their meal. Some residents eat much more slowly than others.

☐ If a resident does not eat well or rejects a food, offer to get a substitute, especially if the resident is underweight or poorly nourished. A resident should never leave the dining room hungry or be given food they cannot eat. Residents should not take food from the dining room to eat later. Unrefrigerated food increases the risk of foodborne illness.

Finish with the following steps:

☐ Determine the resident's preferred position for comfort and ask them if they need anything else.

☐ Examine the environment for safety and cleanliness.

☐ Secure the call light and any other needed items within reach of the resident.

☐ Perform hand hygiene.

☐ Document the procedure and report any findings to the staff in charge.

_____ out of _____ = _____ %   Date: _____

Name: _____   Reviewer: _____

Does the candidate:

☐ Knock on door, introduce self, and address resident by preferred name.

☐ Perform hand hygiene.

☐ Gather supplies and secure assistance if needed.

    ☐ Admission checklist, worksheet, or chart

    ☐ Thermometer

    ☐ Stethoscope

    ☐ Blood pressure gauge

    ☐ A watch with a second hand

    ☐ Scale

    ☐ Urine specimen cup and rubber gloves (if required)

    ☐ Gown or pajamas (if used in your facility)

☐ Explain procedure and ask about resident preferences?

☐ Respect privacy and resident rights at all times?

Continue with the following steps:

☐ Identify the resident and double check the name against any paperwork.

☐ Ask family and friends to wait in the lobby or waiting area.

☐ Assist the nurse as requested.

_____ out of _____ = _____ %

Date: _____

Name: _____

Reviewer: _____

Assisting with Walking

Does the candidate:

☐ Check the care plan.

☐ Knock, introduce self, and address resident by preferred name.

☐ Perform hand hygiene.

☐ Gather supplies and secure assistance as needed:

  ☐ Gait or transfer belt

☐ Explain procedure and ask about resident preferences.

☐ Respect privacy and rights at all times.

Continue with the following steps:

☐ Ensure that the resident is wearing non slip shoes that fit properly before assisting with walking.

☐ Place the gait belt on the resident.

☐ If the resident walks without any type of assistive device, stand at their side so you can see their face as you hold onto the gait belt from behind.

☐ If the resident needs help using a cane, stand on the same side as the hand holding the cane, with one hand on the back of the belt and the other on the cane. Most residents who use a cane can hold it by themselves, so with them, you can stand on the opposite side. Make sure that the resident holds the cane in the correct hand.

☐ If the resident uses a walker, stand at their side, with one hand on the walker if the resident needs help with the walker.

☐ Walk with the resident. Have them take small steps and slowly progress to larger steps, if possible.

☐ When walking in hallways, encourage residents not using a walker to use the safety bars along the wall for added support. Always stand on the side away from the wall so they may use the bars.

☐ When the resident has finished walking, remove the gait belt.

Finish with the following steps:

☐ Determine the resident's preferred position for comfort and ask them if they need anything else.

☐ Examine the environment for safety and cleanliness.

☐ Secure the call light and any items within reach of the resident.

☐ Perform hand hygiene.

☐ Document the procedure and report any findings to the staff in charge.

_____ out of _____ = _____ %   Date: _____

Name: _____   Reviewer: _____

Competency Checklist
Backrub

Does the candidate:

- ☐ Check the care plan.
- ☐ Knock on door, introduce self, and address resident by preferred name.
- ☐ Perform hand hygiene.
- ☐ Gather supplies and secure assistance if needed:
    - ☐ Lotion
    - ☐ A towel
- ☐ Explain procedure and ask about resident preferences.
- ☐ Respect privacy
- ☐ Respect resident rights at all times.
- ☐ Apply gloves, as needed.

Continue with the following steps:

- ☐ Position the resident so that his or her back is toward you.
- ☐ Ensure resident is comfortable.
- ☐ Place the towel lengthwise on the bed next to the resident's back. Observe skin for any reddened or broken areas. If present, call for charge nurse to come and assess before proceeding.
- ☐ Pour a small amount of lotion into the palm of your hand. Rub your hands together to warm the lotion. Explain to the resident what you are doing at each step.
- ☐ Starting with the lower back, massage with gentle motions, working toward the shoulders then downward to the lower back.
- ☐ Use firm pressure as you stroke upward and gentle pressure as you stroke downward. Use a circular motion over the bony areas. It should be one continuous, flowing motion.
- ☐ Continue for three minutes.
- ☐ Pat the resident's back with the towel.
- ☐ Assist the resident with dressing and position the resident comfortably.
- ☐ When finished, gather soiled linen and place in dirty hamper. Remove gloves, if used. Perform hand hygiene.

Finish with the following steps:

- ☐ Determine the resident's preferred position for comfort and ask them if they need anything.
- ☐ Examine the environment for safety and cleanliness.
- ☐ Secure the call light and any other needed items within reach of the resident.
- ☐ Perform hand hygiene.
- ☐ Document the procedure and report any findings to the staff in charge.

_____ out of _____ = _____ %   Date: _____

Name: _____   Reviewer: _____

Competency Checklist

Bringing the Resident to the Unit

Does the candidate:

☐ Calmly escort the resident and family to the room. Don't rush them.

☐ Introduce the new resident and family to any roommates.

☐ Show the new resident around the facility, and explain where things are located. Explain how the lights, the thermostat, the TV, and the nursing call system work.

☐ Assist the resident in making a list of his or her personal possessions.

☐ Assist the new resident into bed or into a chair if he or she is allowed to sit up.

☐ Explain the other areas of the facility. Explain what services are available.

☐ Remind of full life conference schedule and time. Provide contact information for key facility staff.

☐ Explain meal times.

☐ Answer any further questions the resident or family may have, or refer them to the appropriate staff.

One final note: You should always remember how frightened the new resident may feel in the first hours or days in your facility. He or she must not feel you are rushing through the admission to get on to something "more important." Take the time to explain things and be pleasant. Establish yourself as a new friend that the resident can trust.

_____ out of _____ = _____ %   Date: _____

Name: _____   Reviewer: _____

Brushing and Flossing

Does the candidate:

☐ Check the care plan

☐ Knock, introduce self, and address resident by preferred name.

☐ Perform hand hygiene.

☐ Gather supplies and secure assistance if needed:

    ☐ Soft-bristle toothbrush   ☐ Emesis basin   ☐ Dental Floss

    ☐ Toothpaste   ☐ Mouthwash   ☐ Gloves and other PPE as needed

    ☐ 1 to 2 towels   ☐ Cup half filled with cool water

☐ Explain procedure and ask about resident preferences.

☐ Respect privacy at rights at all times.

Continue with the following steps:

Maintain clean technique with toothbrush throughout the procedure.

☐ Wet the toothbrush, apply a small amount of toothpaste, and set it aside. Mix water and mouthwash in a cup. A solution of half water, half mouthwash is best. (Mouthwash is strong and can harm sensitive gums.) Set this aside.

☐ Break off at least 18 inches of floss. Set this aside.

☐ Put on gloves. If you know that the resident's gums bleed, talk with the charge nurse about other personal protective equipment you may need, such as protective goggles and a face mask.

☐ Put a towel over the resident's chest to protect clothing.

☐ Give the resident a small amount of mouthwash solution to swish around to rinse the mouth. Place the emesis basin under the resident's chin so they can spit out the solution after use.

☐ Brush the resident's upper teeth and gums first, moving the brush in a downward direction from the gums to the teeth. Then brush the lower teeth and gums, moving upward from the gums to the teeth. Be sure to brush the back of the teeth. Inspect the teeth and gums while brushing.

☐ Brush the tongue gently.

☐ Help the resident rinse with a small amount of the mouthwash solution.

☐ Wrap the ends of the floss around the middle fingers of each of your hands to get a good grip. Gently insert the floss between each tooth and the next. Move the floss to the gum line and down between the teeth. Wrap the floss around your fingertips so you use a clean section of floss as you move from tooth to tooth.

☐ Have the resident rinse their mouth thoroughly.

☐ Dry off any solution or water around the resident's mouth or chin.

☐ Clean and store equipment.

☐ Remove gloves and any other PPE used. Perform hand hygiene.

Finish with the following steps:

☐ Determine the resident's preferred position for comfort and ask them if they need anything else.

☐ Examine the environment for safety and cleanliness.

☐ Secure the call light and any other needed items within reach of the resident.

☐ Perform hand hygiene.

☐ Document the procedure and report any findings to the staff in charge.

_____ out of _____ = _____ %   Date: _____

Name: _____   Reviewer: _____

Care of Fingernails

Note: Check to see if Resident is Diabetic. If resident is diabetic then nail care should be done by licensed staff.

Does the candidate:

☐ Check the care plan

☐ Knock, introduce self, and address resident by preferred name.

☐ Gather supplies and secure assistance if needed:

☐ nail clippers	☐ lotion	☐ 2 towels
☐ nail file or emery board	☐ basin half filled with warm water	☐ washcloth
☐ an orange wood stick	☐ soap	☐ gloves if needed

☐ Perform hand hygiene.

☐ Explain procedure and ask about resident preferences.

☐ Respect privacy and rights at all times.

Continue with the following steps:

☐ Place the basin of warm water on the over-the-bed table. Have the resident test the water temperature.

☐ Ask the resident to soak their nails in the basing for 3 to 5 minutes.

☐ Put on gloves. Leaving one hand in the water, wash and rinse the resident's other hand. Dry the hand and place it on a dry towel.

☐ Cleanse under the nails using the orange wood stick.

☐ Repeat 3 and 4 for the other hand.

☐ Inspect the resident's hand for cracks in the skin, unusual spots or discoloration, and rough areas.

☐ Trim the resident's fingernails using the nail clipper. Clip nails straight across. Shape and remove rough edges using an emery board or nail file.

☐ Put lotion on the resident's hands and gently massage the hands from fingertips toward the wrists to stimulate circulation.

☐ Remove gloves and perform hand hygiene.

☐ Tell the nurse about any redness, irritation, broken skin, or loose skin you have observed.

Finish with the following steps:

☐ Determine the resident's preferred position for comfort and ask them if they need anything else.

☐ Examine the environment for safety and cleanliness.

☐ Secure the call light and any other needed items within reach of the resident.

☐ Perform hand hygiene.

☐ Document the procedure and report any findings to the staff in charge.

_____ out of _____ = _____ %   Date: _____

Name: _____   Reviewer: _____

Competency Checklist
Caring for Dentures

Does the candidate:

☐ Check the care plan.

☐ Knock on door, introduce self, and address resident by preferred name?

☐ Perform hand hygiene.

☐ Gather supplies and secure assistance if needed:

    ☐ Denture cup or plastic cup half filled with cool water

    ☐ Mouthwash, according to resident preferences

    ☐ Swab moistened with water and mouthwash

    ☐ 1-2 pairs of gloves

    ☐ 1 or 2 towels

    ☐ Denture cleaning paste or mild toothpaste, that is safe to use on dentures

    ☐ Denture adhesive, per resident preference

    ☐ Paper towels

    ☐ Emesis basin

☐ Explain procedure and ask about resident preferences.

☐ Respect privacy and resident rights at all times.

Continue with the following steps:

If the resident has a partial plate with only a few artificial teeth, handle it using the steps shown below for complete set of dentures. Be careful when you remove the partial plate, which has wires that support the teeth in place. Maintain clean technique with the placement of dentures and toothbrush throughout this procedure.

☐ Put on gloves. Place a towel over the resident's chest.

☐ Before handling dentures, protect dentures from possible breakage (e.g., by lining sink/ basin with a towel/washcloth or by filling it with water; if filling the sink with water, does not float or immerse the dentures in the water.

☐ Ask the resident to remove their dentures and place them in the denture cup. If the resident cannot remove their own dentures, remove them using the following steps.

    ☐ Rinse the resident's mouth with mouthwash solution to moisten it. Ask them to swish the solution around, and put the emesis basin under the chin so the resident can spit out the solution.

    ☐ Remove the upper denture using a paper towel for a better grip. Loosen the denture by gently rocking it back and forth to help break the seal. Put it in the denture cup.

    ☐ Remove lower denture using a paper towel for a better grip. Loosen it by gently rocking it back and forth. Put it in the denture cup.

☐ Rinse the resident's mouth with mouthwash solution.

☐ If the resident cannot rinse, use a swab moistened with water and mouthwash to clean the entire mouth, including the tongue and gums.

☐ Explain that you will clean the dentures and then return them.

☐ Take the denture cup with dentures, toothbrush, and toothpaste to the resident's bathroom.

☐ Put the denture cleaning paste on the toothbrush. Make sure that the paste used is one specially for dentures.

☐ Turn on cool water, put a small towel or face cloth on the bottom of the sink, and fill sink halfway.

☐ Hold the dentures over the sink and brush all surfaces.

☐ Rinse the dentures with cool water. Rinse denture cup and lid.

☐ Return dentures to the denture cup.

☐ If the resident uses adhesive, apply it to the dentures before putting them back in the mouth. If the resident does not want the dentures put back at this time, store them safely. Put them in a denture cup half filled with cool water and labeled with the resident's name.

☐ Inspect the resident's mouth for dryness, bleeding, sores, a dry tongue, or mouth odor. Remove the towel from the resident's chest. Remove gloves and perform hand hygiene. Report any changes to the nurse.

☐ Clean and store equipment.

☐ Remove gloves and performs hand hygiene.

Finish with the following steps:

☐ Determine the resident's preferred position for comfort and ask them if they need anything.

☐ Examine the environment for safety and cleanliness.

☐ Secure the call light and any other needed items within reach of the resident.

☐ Perform hand hygiene.

☐ Document the procedure and report any findings to the staff in charge.

_____ out of _____ = _____ %   Date: _____

Name: _____   Reviewer: _____

Competency Checklist
Collecting a Sputum Specimen

Does the candidate:

☐ Check care plan.

☐ Gather supplies and secure assistance if needed:

　☐ Gloves

　☐ Specimen container and label

　☐ Specimen bag (biohazardous bag)

☐ Knock, introduce self, and address resident by preferred name.

☐ Perform hand hygiene.

☐ Explain procedure and ask about resident preferences.

☐ Respect privacy and rights at all times.

Continue with the following steps:

Make sure that a resident who chews tobacco has not done so before you collect the specimen. If the resident has just eaten, ask them to rinse out their mouth. Try to collect the specimen in the morning. Often, large amounts of sputum are coughed up first thing in the morning.

☐ Put on gloves and give the resident the sputum collection container or hold it yourself. Take care not to touch its inside surface.

☐ Ask the resident to take several deep breaths and cough deeply from the chest. They may need to cough several times to get enough sputum for the sample. Ask them to try not to spit only saliva into the container.

☐ Place the lid securely on the specimen container. Label it with the resident's name, room number, and the date and time of collection. Place the specimen in a biohazardous bag. Explain to the resident what you are going to do.

☐ Remove gloves and perform hand hygiene.

☐ Report the color, amount, and consistency of the specimen to the charge nurse.

☐ Take the labeled specimen to the charge nurse.

Finish with the following steps:

☐ Determine the resident's preferred position for comfort and ask them if they need anything else.

☐ Examine the environment for safety and cleanliness.

☐ Secure the call light and any other needed items within reach of the resident.

☐ Perform hand hygiene.

☐ Document the procedure and report any findings to the staff in charge.

_____ out of _____ = _____ %   Date: _____

Name: _____   Reviewer: _____

Competency Checklist
Collecting a Stool Specimen

Candidate should complete the following steps:

☐ Check care plan.

☐ Gather supplies and secure assistance if needed:

    ☐ 2 pairs of gloves   ☐ Specimen bag (biohazardous bag)

    ☐ Specimen container and label   ☐ Wooden tongue depressor

☐ Knock, introduce self, and address resident by preferred name.

☐ Perform hand hygiene.

☐ Explain procedure and ask about resident preferences.

☐ Respect privacy and rights at all times.

Continue with the following steps:

☐ Put on gloves.

☐ Have the resident use a clean bedpan or receptacle to have a bowel movement. Instructing them not to urinate in the specimen.

☐ When the resident has finished, remove the bedpan and assist with perineal care if needed.

☐ Use the tongue depressor to transfer the stool to the specimen container. Dispose of tongue depressor.

☐ Place the lid securely on the specimen container. Label it with the resident's name, room number, and the date and time of collection. Place the specimen in a biohazardous bag. Empty, clean, and store bedpan.

☐ Wash the bedpan, and put it away.

☐ Remove and dispose of your gloves and preform hand hygiene.

☐ Put on gloves.

☐ Assist the resident in hand hygiene.

☐ Remove gloves and perform hand hygiene.

☐ Report the color, amount, and consistency of the specimen to the charge nurse.

☐ Take the labeled specimen to the charge nurse.

Finish with the following steps:

☐ Determine the resident's preferred position for comfort and ask them if they need anything else.

☐ Examine the environment for safety and cleanliness.

☐ Secure the call light and any other needed items within reach of the resident.

☐ Perform hand hygiene.

☐ Document the procedure and report any findings to the staff in charge.

_____ out of _____ = _____ %   Date: _____

Name: _____   Reviewer: _____

Collecting a Urine Specimen

Does the candidate:

☐ Check the care plan?

☐ Gather supplies and secure assistance as needed:

    ☐ a bedpan, urinal, or toilet hat   ☐ Biohazard bag

    ☐ a specimen container and lid with label   ☐ Disposable trash bag

    ☐ At least 2 pairs of gloves   ☐ Cleaning solution (if needed)

☐ Knock on door, introduce self, and address resident by preferred name.

☐ Perform hand hygiene.

☐ Explain procedure and ask about resident preferences.

☐ Respect privacy and resident rights at all times.

Continue with the following steps:

Remember — if you contaminate your gloves in any way during the procedure, you must change to a new pair.

☐ Have the resident urinate into a clean bedpan, urinal, or toilet hat. Ask the resident to place toilet tissue in the place bag provided, not in the urine specimen.

☐ Pour about 60cc's of urine into the specimen container, discarding remaining urine in the toilet.

☐ Close the container securely, and write the resident's name, room number, and the date and time the specimen was collected on the container label.

☐ Place the specimen container in a biohazard specimen bag and make sure it is properly sealed.

☐ Remove gloves and perform hand hygiene.

Finish with the following steps:

☐ Determine the resident's preferred position for comfort and ask them if they need anything else.

☐ Examine the environment for safety and cleanliness.

☐ Secure the call light and any other needed items within reach of the resident.

☐ Perform hand hygiene.

☐ Document the procedure and report any findings to the staff in charge.

☐ Take the labeled specimen to the charge nurse.

_____ out of _____ = _____ %   Date: _____

Name: _____   Reviewer: _____

Competency Checklist

Complete Bed Bath

Does the candidate:

☐ Check the care plan.

☐ Knock, introduce self, and address resident by preferred name.

☐ Perform hand hygiene.

☐ Gather supplies and secure assistance as needed:

    ☐ At least 3 washcloths

    ☐ At least 2 towels

    ☐ Basin half filled with warm water

    ☐ Soap or preferred body wash

    ☐ Gloves

    ☐ Lotion

    ☐ Waterproof pad

    ☐ Bath blanket

    ☐ Resident's clothing

☐ Explain procedure and ask about resident preferences.

☐ Respect privacy and rights at all times.

Continue with the following steps:

☐ Before beginning the bath, remove the resident's blanket and bedspread and put them on a clean surface.

☐ Place a bath blanket over the top sheet and pull down the top sheet to the foot of the bed, leaving the bath blanket covering the resident.

☐ Remove the resident's clothing under the bath blanket to expose only the part of the body being washed. This allows for privacy and prevents them from becoming cold. The best position for the resident is flat in bed, if they can tolerate it.

☐ Position the resident in a supine position, if the resident is able to tolerate.

☐ Fill the water basin halfway with water that is warm to touch. Test the water with bare hand. ? The water temperature should be 98.6°F to 100°F. Test the water temperature with the inside of the wrist. Then have the resident feel the water to be sure it is comfortable.

☐ Make a mitt with the washcloth.

    ☐ After wringing out the wet washcloth, put your hand in the center of the washcloth.

    ☐ Fold the side of the washcloth over from your little finger, and hold the fold with your thumb.

    ☐ Fold the remaining cloth over and hold it firmly with your thumb.

    ☐ Fold the top edge of the cloth down and tuck it into your palm. Hold it with your thumb.

☐ The mitt is now ready to use. Rinse the cloth and refold the mitt as needed during the bath.

☐ Begin with the resident's eyes, using only water — no soap. Start with the eye that is farther from you. With one corner of the washcloth, wash from the inner corner of the eye outward toward the ear. Clean away any crusting that may be stuck to the lower part of the eye. Use another corner of the washcloth to wash the eye that is closest to you. Be sure to move the washcloth from the inner corner of the eye outward.

☐ Wash the resident's face. Some residents prefer not to use soap on the face. In this case, use water only or a facial cleanser that the resident prefers. To wash with soap, wet the washcloth and apply a small amount of soap. Wash the face and be sure to rinse off all the soap. When you dry the resident's skin, pat it dry, being careful not to rub too hard. Once dry, inspect the area.

☐ Wash the resident's ears and neck. Making sure to wash behind and inside the ear (gently). Wring out washcloth so that excessive waster does not enter the ear canal. Rinse, dry, and inspect the area.

☐ Wash the arms, underarms, and hands. Exposing only the areas that are to be washed. Use soap sparingly. Wash the side away from you first, then the side near you, so that you are moving from a clean area to a dirty area, unless you feel you have to stretch too far and might injure yourself. Rinse, dry and inspect the area.

☐ Fold the bath blanket down and cover the resident's chest with a towel. Wash the chest and the abdomen as far as the pubic area. Pay particular attention to the skin under a female resident's breasts and or any skin folds on the chest and abdomen. Note any redness, odor, or skin breakdown. Cover the chest with the bath blanket.

☐ Expose one leg and foot. Cover with a towel. Wash the legs and feet. Don't forget to wash between the toes. Rinse, dry, and inspect the area. Repeat for other leg and foot. Check between the toes for any redness, irritation, or cracking of the skin. Note any swelling of the feet and legs.

☐ Cover resident. Change the water at this point or at any time during the bath if the water gets too soapy, or dirty. Check temperature as described earlier in the procedure. Follow safety procedures when leaving the bedside.

☐ Help the resident to turn to one side. Keep the resident covered with the bath blanket.

☐ Expose the resident's back and buttocks. Wash the resident's back and buttocks. Rinse dry and inspect the area.

☐ Provide back rub (see Backrub Competency Checklist).

☐ Help position the resident on their back.

☐ Cover resident and change water. Check temperature as described earlier in the procedure. Follow safety procedures when leaving the bedside.

☐ Before performing perineal care, put on gloves and place a waterproof pad under the resident.

Perineal Care for Females

☐ Drape the resident by folding back the bath blanket to expose only her legs and perineal area. Ask the resident to bend knees.

☐ Have the resident check the water temperature to make sure that it is not too warm.

☐ Apply soap to a wet washcloth.

☐ Wash perineal area using downward strokes from the front to the back on each side of the labia. Make sure to use a clean area of the washcloth with each stroke.

- ☐ Wash downward in the middle over the urethra and vaginal opening. Always wash downward toward the anus with a clean area of the cloth to prevent the spread of infection.

- ☐ Using a second clean washcloth, rinse the soap from the perineal area, using the same technique. Wipe from to back using a clean area of the washcloth with each stroke.

- ☐ Dry perineal area with a towel, and inspect for any redness, swelling, odor, drainage, or areas of irritation.

- ☐ After washing the perineal area, turn the resident onto her side and wash and rinse the anal area, moving with upward strokes toward the back. Make sure to use a clean area of the washcloth for each stroke.

- ☐ Dry with a clean towel.

- ☐ Reposition the resident for comfort and remove waterproof pad.

- ☐ Remove gloves and perform hand hygiene.

Perineal Care for Males

- ☐ Drape the resident to expose only the legs and perineal area by folding back the bath blanket. Have the resident check the water temperature to make sure that it is not too warm.

- ☐ Apply soap to a wet washcloth. Wash the penis from the urethral opening or tip of the penis toward the base of the penis (use a clean areas of the washcloth with each downward stroke), and then wash the scrotum. Take care to wash, rinse, and dry between any skin folds. Pull back the foreskin on uncircumcised males and clean under it. Return the foreskin to its natural position. Check for any redness, swelling, or areas of irritation.

- ☐ Help the resident turn onto his side. Wash, rinse, and dry the anal area, moving upward toward the back.

- ☐ Reposition the resident for comfort and remove the waterproof pad.

- ☐ Remove gloves and perform hand hygiene.

☐ Help the resident get dressed.

Finish with the following steps:

☐ Determine the resident's preferred position for comfort and ask them if they need anything else.

☐ Examine the environment for safety and cleanliness.

☐ Secure the call light and any other needed items within reach of the resident.

☐ Perform hand hygiene.

☐ Document the procedure and report any findings to the staff in charge.

_____ out of _____ = _____ %   Date: _____

Name: _____   Reviewer: _____

Competency Checklist
First Aid for Choking

To assist a choking resident, candidate must do the following steps:

☐ Ask resident if they are choking. If the resident can speak or cough do not initiate.

☐ If unable to speak or cough, stand behind a resident who is standing or sitting, and place your arms around the resident's waist. Lean the resident slightly forward.

☐ Call for help.

☐ Make a fist with one hand, and place it on the resident's stomach below the rib cage and a little above the navel. Keep your thumb on their stomach, and place your other hand over your fist.

☐ Sharply thrust your fist inward and upward.

☐ Repeat until the blockage is dislodged.

For a person who has become unconscious after choking:

☐ If the resident is not already on the floor, gently lower them to the floor and call for help.

☐ Position resident on their back. Kneel by the resident's side.

☐ CPR should be initiated based on resident directives and facility policy

☐ Medical staff may ask you to monitor and assist with CPR, depending on facility policy and your training.

☐ Perform hand hygiene

☐ Document and report any findings to the staff in charge

_____ out of _____ = _____ %   Date: _____

Name: _____   Reviewer: _____

Does the candidate:

☐ Check care plan.

☐ Knock, introduce self, and address resident by preferred name.

☐ Perform hand hygiene.

☐ Gather equipment and secure assistance if needed:

☐ Gloves
☐ Washcloth
☐ Soap

☐ 2 towels
☐ Basin half filled with warm water
☐ Orange wood stick

☐ Lotion
☐ Resident's shoes and socks or stockings

☐ Explain procedure and ask about resident preferences.

☐ Respect privacy and rights at all times.

Continue with the following steps:

☐ Put on gloves and help the resident remove shoes and socks or stockings.

☐ To give foot care to a resident sitting in a chair, put a towel on the floor and the basin of water on the towel. Foot care can also be done while a resident is in bed, usually during a bed bath. Put a towel on the bed and the basin on the towel. Ask the resident to flex the leg to soak one foot at a time (3 to 5 minutes each).

☐ For seated residents, place both feet in the basin of warm water and soak for 3 to 5 minutes.

☐ Clean under the toenails with the orange wood stick. Scrub callused areas with a warm wash cloth.

☐ Wash, rinse, dry, and inspect the feet thoroughly. Report any redness, irritation, or cracked, broken, loose, dry, or discolored skin. Report any callused areas, corns, or loose or broken nails.

☐ Apply lotion to the tops of the feet, soles of the feet, and heels. Do not apply lotion between the toes.

☐ Remove gloves and perform hand hygiene.

☐ Help the resident put on clean socks or stockings and shoes.

☐ Tell the charge nurse if the resident needs toenail trimming or care for corns, calluses, or other foot problems.

Finish with the following steps:

☐ Determine the resident's preferred position for comfort and ask them if they need anything else.

☐ Examine the environment for safety and cleanliness.

☐ Secure the call light and any other needed items within reach of the resident.

☐ Perform hand hygiene.

☐ Document the procedure and report any findings to the staff in charge.

_____ out of _____ = _____ %   Date: _____

Name: _____   Reviewer: _____

Competency Checklist

Giving a Modified Bed Bath and Applying Lotion

Does the candidate:

☐ Check the care plan.

☐ Knock, introduce self, and address resident by preferred name.

☐ Perform hand hygiene.

☐ Gather supplies and secure assistance as needed:

    ☐ At least 3 washcloths

    ☐ At least 2 towels

    ☐ Basin half filled with warm water

    ☐ Soap or preferred body wash

    ☐ Gloves

    ☐ Lotion

    ☐ Plastic-covered pad or protective covering

    ☐ Bath blanket

    ☐ Resident's clothing of choice

☐ Perform hand hygiene.

☐ Explain procedure and ask about resident preferences.

☐ Respect privacy and rights at all times.

Continue with the following steps:

☐ Remove or fold back top bedding, keeping client covered with bath blanket (or top sheet).

☐ Remove resident's gown. Avoid unnecessary exposure of resident throughout the modified bed bath.

☐ Test water temperature and ensure it is safe and comfortable before bathing resident, and adjust as necessary.

☐ Wash face with wet washcloth (no soap) beginning with the eyes, using a different area of the washcloth for each eye, washing inner aspect to outer aspect.

☐ Contain corners of washcloth while washing and rinsing (forming mitt).

☐ Dry face with towel, using a blotting motion.

☐ Protect bedding by repositioning towel under resident throughout washing and rinsing.

☐ Wash neck, hands, arms, and chest using small amount of soap applied directly to washcloth (avoid soap applied directly into bath basin). Move resident's body gently and naturally, avoiding force and over-extension of limbs and joints throughout the procedure.

☐ Rinse neck, hands, arms, and chest, removing soap residue.

☐ Dry neck, hands, arm, and chest.

☐ Ask and assist resident to turn on side. Ask resident if he/she can assist you by holding onto the side rail.

☐ Wash, rinse, and dry back.

☐ Assess resident for any reddened areas, open wounds, or dressings before applying lotion. If present, notify nurse before proceeding.

☐ Warm lotion in hands before applying to resident's back, arms, legs and feet.

☐ Provide backrub using strokes to cover from base of spine and working towards neck and shoulders using gentle strokes and circular motions.

☐ Remove unabsorbed excess lotion on resident's back.

☐ Put clean gown on client and secure gown in the back.

☐ Remove bath blanket and pull up bedcovers.

☐ Before leaving resident, place call button within resident's reach.

☐ Empty, rinse, and wipe bath basin, and return to proper storage.

☐ Dispose of soiled linen in soiled linen container.

☐ Perform hand hygiene.

Finish with the following steps:

☐ Determine the resident's preferred position for comfort and ask them if they need anything else.

☐ Examine the environment for safety and cleanliness.

☐ Secure the call light and any items within reach of the resident.

☐ Perform hand hygiene.

☐ Document the procedure and report any findings to the staff in charge.

_____ out of _____ = _____ %   Date: _____

Name: _____   Reviewer: _____

Guidelines for Feeding Most Residents

Does the candidate:

☐ Check the care plan.

☐ Knock, introduce self, and address resident by preferred name.

☐ Perform hand hygiene.

☐ Gather supplies and secure assistance if needed.

☐ Explain procedure and ask about resident preferences.

☐ Respect privacy and rights at all times.

Continue with the following steps:

☐ Prepare resident for their meal.

☐ Provide oral care, wash the resident's hands, and make him/her comfortable.

☐ Check the resident's positioning. Elevate the head of the bed to at least 75 to 90 degrees, if in bed. If in chair ensure resident is in an upright sitting position before feeding resident? Cover the resident with a clothing protector or a large napkin, if requested by the resident.

☐ Check the tray card to ensure the accuracy of the meal being served.

☐ Remove foods from the tray, place them on the table in front of the resident, and describe each one. Encourage residents to help themselves in any way possible, such as by holding their own cup.

☐ Sit next to the resident while feeding them, making eye contact. Use a spoon from which the resident can easily remove the food. Usually a teaspoon is better than a larger soup spoon, Fill the spoon not more than half full. Offer small bites, making sure the resident swallows each bite, before offering another. Feed residents in a manner as close to normal as possible to preserve their dignity. Speak softly and maintain eye contact. Let the resident decide what to eat an in what order.

☐ Check the food temperature. If the food seems too hot, give them time to cool. Do not mix foods together unless the resident request this.

☐ Encourage the resident to eat more nutritious foods first (meats, fish, eggs, vegetables, and fresh fruits). Save dessert until last, if possible. Do not rush the resident. Offer liquids between bites to keep their mouth moist.

☐ Maintain a caring attitude, and encourage the resident to eat all of their meal. Offer to get a substitute if they are not eating or refuse a certain food.

☐ When the resident is finished eating, remove the clothing protector, any remaining food, and the tray.

☐ Provide oral care.

☐ Report to the charge nurse any changes that occur with feeding, such as the resident experiencing nausea, stomach pain, or discomfort, choking, or decreased appetite.

Finish with the following steps:

☐ Determine the resident's preferred position for comfort and ask them if they need anything else.

☐ Examine the environment for safety and cleanliness.

☐ Secure the call light and any items within reach of the resident.

☐ Perform hand hygiene.

☐ Document the procedure and report any findings to the staff in charge.

_____ out of _____ = _____ %   Date: _____

Name: _____   Reviewer: _____

Competency Checklist
Hair Care

Does the candidate:

☐ Check care plan

☐ Knock, introduce self, and address resident by preferred name.

☐ Perform hand hygiene.

☐ Gather equipment and secure assistance if needed:

    ☐ Hair brush or comb

    ☐ Styling products, per resident preferences.

    ☐ Mirror

    ☐ Personal items for styling

☐ Explain procedure and ask about resident preferences.

☐ Respect privacy and rights at all times.

Continue with the following steps:

☐ Brush hair gently. If the resident's hair is long and tangled, gently remove tangles with a wide-tooth comb before brushing. Start at the ends and work your way up to the scalp.

☐ Gently brush and style the hair to the resident's preference. Use any personal items they may request, such as hair clips or styling products. Give the resident a mirror so they can view their hair and confirm that they are satisfied with their appearance.

Finish with the following steps:

☐ Determine the resident's preferred position for comfort and ask them if they need anything else.

☐ Examine the environment for safety and cleanliness.

☐ Secure the call light and any other needed items within reach of the resident.

☐ Perform hand hygiene.

☐ Document the procedure and report any findings to the staff in charge.

_____ out of _____ = _____ %   Date: _____

Name: _____   Reviewer: _____

Does the candidate:

☐ Before you begin, check to make sure that the sink is clean and the soap dispenser is in reach. Paper towels must be within reach without touching the dispenser.

☐ Remove watch and roll up sleeves.

☐ Turn on water and adjust to a comfortable temperature. Wet hands and wrists.

☐ Apply or soap to hands.

☐ Rub hands together in a circular motion with friction for a minimum of 20 seconds.

☐ Clean all surfaces of your hands, including your wrists. Lace your fingers together to wash in between them. Clean under fingernails using a nail brush or orange stick, or rub your nails briskly in your palm to clean them.

☐ Rinse hands and wrists with warm water, keeping them downward allowing the water to run from the wrists to the fingers.

☐ Get paper towels from the dispenser. Touch only the clean towels, not the dispenser.

☐ Dry hands with paper towels. Start at the top of the fingers and work toward the wrist

☐ Turn off faucet, using a clean paper towel.

☐ Discard paper towels in appropriate receptacle.

_____ out of _____ = _____ %   Date: _____

Name: _____   Reviewer: _____

Helping a Male Resident Use a Urinal

Candidate should follow these steps:

☐ Check the care plan

☐ Knock, introduce self, and address resident by preferred name.

☐ Perform hand hygiene.

☐ Gather supplies and secures assistance if needed:

　　☐ Urinal

　　☐ Wash basin

　　☐ Towel

　　☐ Soap

　　☐ Toilet paper

　　☐ At least three pairs of gloves

　　☐ Waterproof pad or protective cover

☐ Explain the procedure and ask about resident preferences.

☐ Respect privacy and rights at all times.

Continue with the following steps:

☐ Put on gloves.

☐ Put a pad or cover on the surface where you will put the urinal after use.

☐ If the resident can stand beside the bed to use the urinal after you use it.

☐ If the resident can stand beside the bed to use the urinal, help him to stand, and provide privacy. Put the call light within reach so he can call you when finished.

☐ If the resident must use the urinal while in bed, fold the bedspread and blanket down to the bottom of the bed, leaving the top sheet over the resident. Help the resident lower his bottom clothing. Place waterproof pad under resident.

☐ Place the urinal between the resident's legs at an angle to avoid urinal spillage. Gently place the penis into the urinal.

☐ Remove your gloves and put them in the trash bag. Perform hand hygiene. Cover the resident with the top sheet. Put the call button within reach so he can call you when finished. Check in a few minutes if he does not call you.

☐ When the resident calls, perform hand hygiene and put on gloves.

☐ When the resident is finished, remove the urinal and place it on waterproof pad or protective cover.

☐ If needed, help the resident wipe off excess urine with toilet tissue.

☐ Remove gloves and perform hand hygiene.

☐ Put on gloves.

☐ Assist the resident with hand hygiene.

☐ Empty and clean the urinal (being careful not to splash contents) and replace it in the bedside table (or store per facility policy).

☐ Remove and dispose of toilet tissue and gloves and place them in the disposable trash bag.

☐ Perform hand hygiene.

Finish with the following steps:

☐ Determine the resident's preferred position for comfort and ask them if they need anything else.

☐ Examine the environment for safety and cleanliness.

☐ Secure the call light and any items within reach of the resident.

☐ Perform hand hygiene.

☐ Document the procedure and report any findings to the staff in charge.

_____ out of _____ = _____ %   Date: _____

Name: _____   Reviewer: _____

Helping a Resident Use a Bedpan

Does the candidate:

☐ Check the care plan.

☐ Knock, introduce self, and address resident by preferred name.

☐ Perform hand hygiene.

☐ Gather supplies and secure assistance as needed:

 ☐ Bedpan with cover

 ☐ At least 2 washcloths

 ☐ At least 2 towels

 ☐ Wash basin half filled with water

 ☐ Toilet paper

 ☐ Soap

 ☐ At least three pairs of gloves

 ☐ Waterproof pad or protective covering

☐ Explain procedure and ask about resident preferences.

☐ Respect privacy and rights at all times.

Continue with the following steps:

Remember — if you contaminate your gloves in any way during the procedure, you must change to a new pair.

☐ Put on gloves.

☐ Place the protective covering or pad where you will put the bedpan.

☐ Fold the bedspread and blanket to the both of the bed, leaving the top sheet in place to cover the resident's lower legs. Help thee resident remove or adjust clothing so bedpan can be placed under the resident.

☐ Before placing bedpan, lower head of bed.

☐ Place protective pad under the resident's buttocks to protect bed linens.

☐ Ask the resident to bend their knees and lift their buttocks up while you slide the bedpan underneath them. Adjust for the resident's comfort. If the resident is unable to lift their buttocks on their own, you can help them turn onto one side. Hold the bedpan flush against the buttocks. Have the resident turn back onto the bedpan or help them move back onto the bedpan. For standard bedpan, position bedpan so wider end of pan is aligned with resident's buttocks. For fracture pan, position bedpan with handle toward the foot of the bed.

☐ Remove gloves and perform hand hygiene.

☐ Cover the resident with the top sheet.

☐ Elevate the head of the bed slowly until the resident is in a sitting position. Ask the resident if they are comfortable. Change the position of the bedpan if needed to make the resident more comfortable.

☐ Provide toilet paper and position call light button so the resident can reach it.

☐ Ask resident to signal when finished. Check on them every five minutes. The bedpan puts pressure on the skin, do not leave them on the bedpan longer than necessary.

☐ Perform hand hygiene.

☐ Once the resident is finished with elimination, put on gloves.

☐ Lower head of bed. Ask the resident to lift their buttocks up while your slide the bedpan out. If needed, help them roll onto their side while you hold the bedpan to prevent a spill. Move the bedpan to the covered surface.

☐ If needed, help with wiping the perineal area or provide perineal care. Put the used toilet paper in the bedpan. Remove and dispose of the protective pad from under the resident's buttocks.

☐ Remove gloves and perform hand hygiene. Put on gloves.

☐ Assist the resident with hand hygiene.

☐ Remove gloves and perform hand hygiene. Put on gloves.

☐ Help the resident get dressed.

☐ Cover the bedpan and dispose of the contents into toilet.

☐ Clean the bedpan (being careful not to splash contents) and return it to the bedside table (or store per facility policy). Remove and dispose of the protective pad on which you placed the bedpan.

☐ Remove gloves and perform hand hygiene.

Finish with the following steps:

☐ Determine the resident's preferred position for comfort and ask them if they need anything else.

☐ Examine the environment for safety and cleanliness.

☐ Secure the call light and any items within reach of the resident.

☐ Perform hand hygiene.

☐ Document the procedure and report any findings to the staff in charge.

_____ out of _____ = _____ %   Date: _____

Name: _____   Reviewer: _____

Helping a Resident Use a Portable Commode

Candidate should follow these steps:

☐ Check care plan.

☐ Knock, introduce self, and address resident by preferred name.

☐ Perform hand hygiene.

☐ Gather equipment and secure assistance if needed:

    ☐ At least 2 pairs of gloves   ☐ Toilet paper   ☐ Soap

    ☐ Wash basin half filled with warm water   ☐ Towel

☐ Explain procedure and ask about resident preferences.

☐ Respect privacy and rights at all times.

Continue with the following steps:

☐ Remember — if you contaminate your gloves in any way during the procedure, you must change to a new pair.

☐ Position the commode by the bed. Place it so it will not move when you help the resident out of bed. You can place it against the wall or against the bedside table to keep it from moving.

☐ Put on gloves.

☐ Help the resident out of bed or out of a chair to a standing position. Help pull down the resident's lower clothing, and help them sit on the commode.

☐ Provide toilet paper and put the call button within reach. Remove gloves and perform hand hygiene.

☐ If the resident needs help with wiping when finished, first put on gloves. Help with wiping, and throw the tissue into the commode or place in the trash bag.

☐ Remove your gloves and dispose of them in the trash bag. Perform hand hygiene.

☐ Help the resident with their clothing and to get back into the bed or chair.

☐ Put on gloves.

☐ Help the resident perform hand hygiene.

☐ Remove the container from the commode and empty its contents into the resident's toilet. Most facilities have a water sprayer attached to the toilet. Follow your facility's procedures for using this equipment. When you empty and clean the commode container, be careful not to splash the contents.

☐ Clean and dry the container and replace it in the commode.

☐ Remove your gloves and place them in the disposable trash bag. Properly dispose of the trash bag, and perform hand hygiene.

Finish with the following steps:

☐ Determine the resident's preferred position for comfort and ask them if they need anything else.

☐ Examine the environment for safety and cleanliness.

☐ Secure the call light and any other needed items within reach of the resident.

☐ Perform hand hygiene.

☐ Document the procedure and report any findings to the staff in charge.

_____ out of _____ = _____ %   Date: _____

Name: _____   Reviewer: _____

Competency Checklist

Log Rolling

Does the candidate:

☐ Check the care plan.

☐ Knock, introduce self, and address resident by preferred name.

☐ Perform hand hygiene.

☐ Gather supplies and secure assistance as needed.

☐ Explain procedure and ask about resident preferences.

☐ Respect privacy and rights at all times.

Continue with the following steps:

☐ Use a lift sheet and the help of a co-worker to move the resident to the side of the bed.

☐ Using the sheet as support, grasp the sheet at the shoulder and hip on the side closest to the edge of the bed.

☐ Pull the sheet and roll the resident to the center of the bed into the desired position. Your co-worker should help with the knees and ensure that body alignment is maintained throughout the procedure.

☐ Adjust resident for comfort, using pillows as needed.

Finish with the following steps:

☐ Determine the resident's preferred position for comfort and ask them if they need anything else.

☐ Examine the environment for safety and cleanliness.

☐ Secure the call light and any items within reach of the resident.

☐ Perform hand hygiene.

☐ Document the procedure and report any findings to the staff in charge.

_____ out of _____ = _____ %   Date: _____

Name: _____   Reviewer: _____

Making an Occupied Bed

Does the candidate:

☐ Check the care plan.

☐ Knock, introduce self, and address resident by preferred name.

☐ Perform hand hygiene.

☐ Gather supplies and secure assistance as needed:

    ☐ One fitted sheet and a flat sheet, or two flat sheets   ☐ Pillow cases   ☐ Bedspread

    ☐ Draw or lift sheet if used   ☐ Blanket   ☐ Gloves

☐ Explain procedure and ask about resident preferences.

☐ Respect privacy and rights at all times.

☐ Lower the head of the bed, and remove the pillow from under the resident's head, if resident is comfortable and able to tolerate a flat position.

☐ Remove the bedspread and any blankets. Fold them and place them on the chair.

☐ Loosen the top and bottom sheets from under the mattress.

☐ Help the resident roll over on their side toward you. Make sure the resident stays covered throughout the procedure. Raise the side rail and ask them to hold on for support, as appropriate.

☐ Move around to the other side of the bed.

☐ Check for personal belongings in the bed.

☐ Wear gloves, as necessary. Roll lengthwise (top to bottom) the soiled bottom sheet from the side of the mattress to the center of the bed close to the resident's body. (If the linen is damp or wet, place a barrier over the sheet).

To Replace a Fitted Sheet:

☐ Starting at the top corner of the mattress, fit the corner of the sheet over the edge of the mattress, then go to the bottom of the bed on the same side and fit the sheet over that edge. Be sure half of the mattress is covered and the sheet is tucked close to the resident.

☐ If using a draw sheet, place it in the center of the bed so it covers the middle part of the bed and is tucked close to the resident. Tuck in the draw sheet on the side you are working. You may also place any needed disposable incontinence pads over the draw sheet.

To Use a Flat Sheet as the Bottom Sheet:

☐ Unfold the flat sheet lengthwise down the center of the bed. Do not shake the linen while unfolding it.

☐ Place the hem seams toward the mattress.

☐ Slide the sheet so that the hem is even with the foot of the mattress. Keep the fold in the exact center of the bed. (You want the extra length at the top to tuck it under the mattress).

☐ Open the sheet and fan-fold it lengthwise so that one half of the sheet is next to the rolled dirty sheet.

☐ Tuck the top hem in tightly under the mattress at the head of the bed by lifting the mattress edge and sliding the sheet under it.

☐ Make a mitered corner. Face the side of the bed, and lay it on top of the bed so it looks like a triangle. Tuck the remaining sheet under the mattress. Drop the section of sheets from on top of the bed over the side of the bed, and tuck it in. Repeat for other three corners.

☐ Tuck the remaining sheet under the mattress neatly.

☐ If you are using a draw sheet, place it in the center of the bed so it covers the middle part of the bed. Fan-fold the excess and tuck it in with the sheet. Tuck in the draw sheet.

☐ Flatten the rolled or fan-folded sheets and help the resident roll over the linen toward you, using the correct procedure for turning them. Don't forget first to remind the resident that the roll of linen is behind them.

☐ Move to the opposite side of the bed, lower the side rail, remove the dirty linen, and place it in the laundry bag. Never leave the resident unattended to take away the dirty laundry.

☐ Pull the clean linen toward you until it is completely unfolded, and tuck the sheets in tightly the same way as you did the other side.

☐ Tuck in the draw sheet, if used.

☐ Help the resident roll back to the center of the bed.

To Replace the Top Sheet and Bedspread:

☐ Place the top sheet on the bed over the sheet covering the resident. Open the sheet form the fold so that the sheets hangs evenly on each side of the bed. The wide hem should be at the top with the seam on the outside. When you fold the hem over, the smooth side will be next to the resident's skin, preventing any rough edges from touching them. The excess sheet should hang over the foot of the bed.

☐ Ask the resident to hold onto the clean sheet, then carefully remove the dirty tip sheet by placing your hand under the clean top sheet and rolling the dirty sheet down toward the foot of the bed. Remove it and place it with the other dirty linen.

☐ Place the bedspread on top of the sheet in the same way you did the top sheet. Make sure that the sheet does not stick out below the bedspread on the sides.

☐ Tuck in the sheet and bedspread at the foot of the bed, making mitered corners on both sides.

☐ Smooth the sheet and bedspread from the bottom to the top of the bed, and fold down the top hem of the sheet over the bedspread.

☐ Make sure that the top linens are not so tight that they are pressing on the resident's feet. To be sure, make a toe pleat. This is done by pulling the top linen up to from a pleat.

To Replace the Pillow Case:

☐ Hold the center of the closed end of the pillow case with your hand and turn it inside out over your hand.

☐ Grasp the the pillow in your hand inside the pillowcase and slide the case over the pillow. Make sure that the corners of the pillow fit into the corners of the case.

☐ Place the pillow under the resident's head.

Finish with the following steps:

☐ Determine the resident's preferred position for comfort and ask them if they need anything else.

☐ Examine the environment for safety and cleanliness.

☐ Secure the care light and any items within reach of the resident.

☐ Perform hand hygiene.

☐ Document the procedure and report any findings to the staff in charge.

_____ out of _____ = _____ %   Date: _____

Name: _____   Reviewer: _____

Does the candidate:

☐ Check the care plan.

☐ Knock, introduce self, and address resident by preferred name.

☐ Perform hand hygiene.

☐ Gather supplies and secure assistance if needed.

☐ Explain procedure and ask about resident preferences.

☐ Respect privacy and rights at all times.

Continue with the following steps:

☐ Follow facility policy and manufacture guidelines on operating scales

☐ Determine if the resident can walk to the scale or whether you need to bring a portable scale to their room.

☐ Before the resident steps on the scale, adjust the height measurement bar so it is positioned higher that the resident's head.

☐ Ask the resident what their height is and how long ago it was measured.

☐ Clear the scale and make sure it is balanced. It should register zero when the weights are moved all the way to the left.

☐ Place a paper towel on the scale platform, and ask the resident to remove their shoes.

☐ Help the resident step up and stand on the scale. Make sure they are not holding anything.

☐ Have the resident stand up straight, with their arms by their sides and eyes facing forward. Slowly lower the height measurement bar to the top of their head. Record their height in feet and inches.

☐ Measure the resident's weight by moving the weights to the right until the balance needle is centered. If the weight is five pounds or more higher or lower than the previous measurement, weigh the resident a second time to check for accuracy. If this is still the case, report it to the charge nurse. If the resident is wearing a cast or brace while being weighed, note this and report it to the charge nurse.

☐ Help the resident step off the scale.

☐ Record the resident's height and weight report the findings to the charge nurse.

Finish with the following steps:

☐ Determine the resident's preferred position for comfort and ask them if they need anything else.

☐ Examine the environment for safety and cleanliness.

☐ Secure the call light and any other needed items within reach of the resident.

☐ Perform hand hygiene.

☐ Document the procedure and report any findings to the staff in charge.

_____ out of _____ = _____ %   Date: _____

Name: _____   Reviewer: _____

Competency Checklist

Mouth Care for Unconscious Residents

Does the candidate:

☐ Check care plan.

☐ Knock, introduce self, and address resident by preferred name.

☐ Perform hand hygiene.

☐ Gather equipment and secure assistance if needed:

    ☐ Gloves

    ☐ Oral swabs or a soft bristled toothbrush

    ☐ Cup of water or diluted mouthwash, according to resident preference

    ☐ 1 or 2 towels

    ☐ Lip balm or protective jelly

☐ Explain procedure and ask about resident preferences.

☐ Respect privacy and rights at all times.

Continue with the following steps:

☐ Gently turn the resident's head toward you and elevate the head of the bed (if they can tolerate it) to prevent aspiration.

☐ Put a towel over the resident's chest to protect clothing.

☐ Put on gloves.

☐ Gently open the resident's mouth and inspect the mouth, teeth, gums, and tongue for changes or signs of injury: bleeding, sores, loose or broken teeth, dry coated tongue, or mouth odor.

☐ Using an oral swab dipped in water or mouthwash or soft toothbrush, clean the inside of the mouth (gums, tongue, teeth, roof of the mouth, and insides of the cheeks). Tap off excess water/mouthwash. Excess fluid can drip back into the throat and potentially cause aspiration (inhaling fluid or foreign material into the lungs).

☐ Use a towel to dry any solution from around the mouth and chin.

☐ Dispose of used swabs by placing into the plastic trash bag.

☐ Apply protective jelly or lip balm on the resident's lips to moisten them.

☐ Remove towel from resident's chest.

☐ Remove gloves and perform hand hygiene.

Finish with the following steps:

☐ Determine the resident's preferred position for comfort and ask them if they need anything else.

☐ Examine the environment for safety and cleanliness.

☐ Secure the call light and any other needed items within reach of the resident.

☐ Perform hand hygiene.

☐ Document the procedure and report any findings to the staff in charge.

_____ out of _____ = _____ %   Date: _____

Name: _____   Reviewer: _____

Moving and Lifting a Resident Using Proper Body Mechanics

Does the candidate:

☐ Check the care plan

☐ Knock, introduce self, and address resident by preferred name.

☐ Perform hand hygiene

☐ Gather supplies and secures assistance if needed:

    ☐ Gait belt

    ☐ Sliding board, if needed

    ☐ Towel, if needed

☐ Explain procedure and ask about resident preferences.

☐ Respect privacy and rights at all times.

Continue with the following steps:

☐ This process involves three phases, and each phase includes a sequence of steps.

PHASE 1: ASSESS THE SITUATION.

☐ Adjust the height of the bed. Move it up to the height of your elbow when giving care (as when giving a complete bed bath) and down when moving someone out of the bed. Changing the height reduces the amount of bending you have to do.

☐ To avoid reaching injuries, bring any items you need close to you.

☐ If you are moving a resident in bed, consider putting your knee up on the bed. This allows you to get closer to residents without reaching.

☐ You may want to use a friction-reducing device. Place a barrier such as a sheet or towel between your knee and the bed sheets.

PHASE 2: PREPARE YOURSELF.

☐ Place your feet about shoulder-width apart, one foot slightly in front of the other, for a stronger base of support and better stability.

☐ Tighten your abdominal muscles. This supports your spine.

☐ Keep your back neutral.

PHASE 3: DETERMINE HOW TO MOVE, AND EXECUTE THE LIFT.

☐ Get as close as possible to the resident. The "hug" position is very supportive. Use a gait or transfer belt with handles for a secure grip.

☐ Keep your palms up when lifting. Lift from underneath, using your biceps (muscles of the upper arm).

Moving and Lifting a Resident Using Proper Body Mechanics cont.

☐ Inhale deeply before you begin the lift, and exhale while you lift. This helps pump blood and oxygen to your muscles.

☐ Rock to gain momentum for a lift or move. Rocking is moving your body very slightly, either back and forth or side to side. This rocking motion increases your strength.

☐ Bend your knees and lift the resident using your leg, arm, and abdominal muscles, not your back.

☐ Always be careful not to move a resident too quickly, which can cause injury. When possible, use a sliding board as a bridge between the bed and chair and a friction-reducing device.

Finish with the following steps:

☐ Determine the resident's preferred position for comfort and ask them if they need anything else.

☐ Examine the environment for safety and cleanliness.

☐ Secure the call light and any other needed items within reach of the resident.

☐ Document the procedure and report any findings to the staff in charge.

_____ out of _____ = _____ %

Date: _____

Name: _____

Reviewer: _____

Moving Up in Bed When a Resident Can Help

Note: Occasionally, the resident will slide down in bed and will need assistance to pull them back up. Residents should be encouraged to help as much as possible. This will help them to build their muscles, increase circulation, and give them a sense of being in control.

Does the candidate:

☐ Check the care plan

☐ Knock, introduce self, and address resident by preferred name

☐ Perform hand hygiene.

☐ Gather supplies and secure assistance if needed.

☐ Explain procedure and ask about resident preferences.

☐ Respect privacy and rights at all times.

Continue with the following steps:

☐ With the resident lying supine, lower the head of the bed to a flat position (if the person can tolerate it). Move the pillows against the headboard to prevent the resident from injuring their head.

☐ Help the resident bend their knees and place their feet on the bed. Place one arm under the resident's upper back behind the shoulders and the other arm under their upper thighs.

☐ On the count of three, have the resident push down with their feet and lift their buttocks (creating a bridge) while you help move them toward the head of the bed. You may also have their resident help by holding on to the side rails. If side rails are used, sure to lower the rails when you are done.

Finish with the following steps:

☐ Determine the resident's preferred position for comfort and ask them if they need anything else.

☐ Examine the environment for safety and cleanliness.

☐ Secure the call light and any other needed items within reach of the resident.

☐ Perform hand hygiene.

☐ Document the procedure and report any findings to the staff in charge.

_____ out of _____ = _____ %   Date: _____

Name: _____   Reviewer: _____

Moving Up in Bed When a Resident is Unable to Help (Two Assist)

Does the candidate:

☐ Check care plan.

☐ Knock, introduce self, and address resident by preferred name.

☐ Perform hand hygiene.

☐ Gather equipment and secure assistance if needed:

☐ Explain procedure and ask about resident preferences.

☐ Respect privacy and rights at all times.

Continue with the following steps:

☐ Ask another staff person to assist you.

☐ With the resident lying supine, lower the head of the bed to a flat position (if the person can tolerate it). Move the pillows against the headboard to prevent the resident from injuring their head.

☐ Help the resident cross their arms over their chest.

☐ Roll the draw sheet up from the side toward the resident until you and your helper have a tight grip on it with both hands. Keep your palms up if that gives you more strength for moving. (If the linen is soiled, use a barrier to prevent contaminating your uniform.) You can place one knee on the bed to get as close to the resident as possible and to provide more leverage.

☐ On the count of three, you and your helper lift the resident up to the head of the bed, using good body mechanics. You can do this in stages until the resident is in position. If the resident can lift their head off the bed, ask them to do this during the move.

☐ Unroll the draw sheet and tuck it in.

Finish with the following steps:

☐ Determine the resident's preferred position for comfort and ask them if they need anything else.

☐ Examine the environment for safety and cleanliness.

☐ Secure the call light and any other needed items within reach of the resident.

☐ Perform hand hygiene.

☐ Document the procedure and report any findings to the staff in charge.

_____ out of _____ = _____ %   Date: _____

Name: _____   Reviewer: _____

Competency Checklist
Partial Bed Bath

Does the candidate:

☐ Check care plan

☐ Knock, introduce self, and address resident by preferred name.

☐ Perform hand hygiene.

☐ Gather equipment on the bedside table:

    ☐ soap in container   ☐ towel

    ☐ wash cloth   ☐ bath blanket (if available)

    ☐ wash basin half filled with warm water

☐ Explain procedure and ask about resident preferences.

☐ Respect privacy and rights at all times.

Continue with the following steps:

☐ Offer a bedpan or urinal (follow procedure for offering a bedpan)

☐ Remove and fold the bedspread and blankets. Cover the resident with a top sheet or bath blanket.

☐ Assist the resident in removing clothing and jewelry.

☐ Fill the basin two-thirds full with warm water. Ask the resident to test the temperature for comfort.

☐ Ask the resident to wash areas of the body which he or she can easily reach. Step aside for privacy, but remain within area in case resident needs additional assistance.

☐ When resident is finished, empty the basin, rinse, and refill it with clean water. Ask resident to ensure comfortable temperature of water.

☐ Wash, rinse, and dry the areas of the body the resident was unable to reach, following procedures outlined in Complete Bed Bath.

☐ Assist the resident in putting on clean clothing of their choice.

☐ Remove the sheets, and remake the bed with clean linen.

Finish with the following steps:

☐ Determine the resident's preferred position for comfort and ask them if they need anything else.

☐ Examine the environment for safety and cleanliness.

☐ Secure the call light and any other needed items within reach of the resident.

☐ Perform hand hygiene.

☐ Document the procedure and report any findings to the staff in charge.

_____ out of _____ = _____ %   Date: _____

Name: _____   Reviewer: _____

Does the candidate:

☐ Check the care plan.

☐ Knock, introduce self, and address resident by preferred name.

☐ Perform hand hygiene.

☐ Gather supplies and secure assistance as needed:

    ☐ At least 2 washcloths

    ☐ At least 2 towels

    ☐ Basin half filled with water

    ☐ Soap

    ☐ Gloves

    ☐ Waterproof pad or protective covering

    ☐ Bath blanket

☐ Explain procedure and ask about resident preferences.

☐ Respect privacy and rights at all times.

Continue with the following steps:

☐ Fill the water basin halfway with water that is warm to touch. Test the water with bare hand. The water temperature should be 98.6°F to 100°F. Test the water temperature with the inside of the wrist. Then have the resident feel the water to be sure it is comfortable.

☐ Put on gloves.

☐ Place a waterproof pad under the resident.

☐ Drape the resident by folding back the bath blanket to expose only her legs and perineal area. Ask the resident to bend knees.

☐ Apply soap to a wet washcloth.

☐ Wash perineal area using downward strokes from the front to the back on each side of the labia. Make sure to use a clean area of the washcloth with each stroke.

☐ Wash downward in the middle over the urethra and vaginal opening.

☐ Using a second clean washcloth, rinse the soap from the perineal area, using the same technique. Wipe from to back using a clean area of the washcloth with each stroke.

☐ Dry perineal area with a towel, and inspect for any redness, swelling, odor, drainage, or areas of irritation.

☐ After washing the perineal area, turn the resident onto her side and wash and rinse the anal area, moving with upward strokes toward the back. Make sure to use a clean area of the washcloth for each stroke.

☐ Dry with a clean towel.

☐ Reposition the resident for comfort and remove waterproof pad.

☐ Remove gloves and perform hand hygiene.

☐ Put on gloves.

☐ Empty, rinse, and wipe basin and return to proper storage.

☐ Remove and dispose of gloves without contaminating self after returning basin to storage.

☐ Perform hand hygiene.

Finish with the following steps:

☐ Determine the resident's preferred position for comfort and ask them if they need anything else.

☐ Examine the environment for safety and cleanliness.

☐ Secure the call light and any items within reach of the resident.

☐ Perform hand hygiene.

☐ Document the procedure and report any findings to the staff in charge.

_____ out of _____ = _____ %   Date: _____

Name: _____   Reviewer: _____

Perineal Care for Males

Does the candidate:

☐ Check care plan

☐ Knock, introduce self, and address resident by preferred name.

☐ Perform hand hygiene.

☐ Gather equipment and secure assistance if needed:

☐ Waterproof pad	☐ Soap	☐ 2 towels
☐ Wash basin	☐ 2 washcloths	☐ Gloves

☐ Explain procedure and ask about resident preferences.

☐ Respect privacy and right at all times.

Continue with the following steps:

☐ Help position the resident on their back.

☐ Cover resident and change water. Check temperature as described earlier in the procedure.

☐ Before performing perineal care, put on gloves and place a waterproof pad under the resident.

☐ Drape the resident to expose only the legs and perineal area by folding back the bath blanket. Have the resident check the water temperature to make sure that it is not too warm.

☐ Apply soap to a wet washcloth.

☐ Wash the penis from the urethral opening or tip of the penis toward the base of the penis (use a clean areas of the washcloth with each downward stroke), and then wash the scrotum. Take care to wash, rinse, and dry between any skin folds. Pull back the foreskin on uncircumcised males and clean under it. Return the foreskin to its natural position. Check for any redness, swelling, or areas of irritation.

☐ Help the resident turn onto his side. Wash, rinse, and dry the anal area, moving upward toward the back.

☐ Reposition the resident for comfort and remove the waterproof pad.

☐ Remove gloves and perform hand hygiene.

☐ Help the resident get dressed.

Finish with the following steps:

☐ Determine the resident's preferred position for comfort and ask them if they need anything else.

☐ Examine the environment for safety and cleanliness.

☐ Secure the call light and any other needed items within reach of the resident.

☐ Perform hand hygiene.

☐ Document the procedure and report any findings to the staff in charge.

_____ out of _____ = _____ %   Date: _____

Name: _____   Reviewer: _____

Competency Checklist

Positioning a Resident on Their Back (Supine)

Does the candidate:

☐ Check care plan.

☐ Knock, introduce self, and address resident by preferred name.

☐ Perform hand hygiene.

☐ Gather equipment and secure assistance if needed:

☐ Explain procedure and ask about resident preferences.

☐ Respect privacy and rights at all times.

Continue with the following steps:

☐ First, move the resident's trunk and lower body so that their spine is in a neutral position. Do the positioning from the top of the body to the bottom.

☐ Position the resident's head and neck. Place a pillow under the resident's head, neck, and the tops of their shoulders. Do not elevate the head too high. Keep it as close to even with the chest as possible or as is comfortable.

☐ Position the resident's arms. The backs of the shoulders and elbows are common places for pressure injuries in residents who cannot change position by themselves. Vary their arm positions to prevent this. Keep the arms straight and resting on the mattress away from their sides, or bend the arms slightly at the elbow with a pillow between the inner arm and their side so that their arm rests on the pillow and their hand on top of the abdomen. Always support the arms in two places when moving them, and move them gently.

☐ Position the resident's legs. The hips, buttocks, sacrum, and coccyx (the tip of the spine at the buttocks, or "tailbone"), and the backs of the heels are common places for pressure injuries. If a resident has ulcers on a hip, place a towel roll along the hip between the hip and the mattress on the affected side. For redness or ulcers under the heels, support the legs by placing a pillow lengthwise to raise the heels above the bed, or place a towel roll under the legs. Position the resident's legs straight and slightly apart. Always support the legs in two places when moving them, and move them gently. For those residents who tend to keep their legs tightly together or crossed, you may place a pillow between the legs.

☐ If a resident has a cast or splint on a limb, hand, or foot or a swollen arm or leg, you can place a pillow lengthwise to support the affected limb, hand, or foot.

Finish with the following steps:

☐ Determine the resident's preferred position for comfort and ask them if they need anything else.

☐ Examine the environment for safety and cleanliness.

☐ Secure the call light and any other needed items within reach of the resident.

☐ Perform hand hygiene.

☐ Document the procedure and report any findings to the staff in charge.

_____ out of _____ = _____ %   Date: _____

Name: _____   Reviewer: _____

Competency Checklist
Positioning a Resident on Their Side (Side-Lying Position)

Does the candidate:

☐ Check care plan

☐ Knock, introduce self, and address resident by preferred name.

☐ Perform hand hygiene.

☐ Gather equipment and secure assistance if needed:

☐ Explain procedure and ask about resident preferences.

☐ Respect privacy and rights at all times.

Continue with the following steps:

Note that the positions described may be modified for the resident's comfort and to prevent pressure injuries.

☐ Begin with the resident in supine position. Stand on the side to which the resident will be turning.

☐ Help the resident bend their knees.

☐ Place one hand on the resident's shoulder that is farthest from you. Place your other hand on the hip farthest from you. On the count of three, help the resident roll toward you. Position the resident comfortably with proper body alignment.

☐ Position the resident's head and neck. Place a pillow under their head so that the neck is properly aligned and comfortable.

☐ Fold a pillow lengthwise and place it behind the resident's back. Gently push the top edge of the pillow under their side and hip.

☐ Position the resident's arms. Gently pull the arm against the mattress out from under the resident's body if it is not already in front of the body. Place a pillow diagonally under the top arm between the arm and the resident's side. Bend the top arm at the elbow and shoulder to rest the arm comfortably on the pillow.

☐ Position the resident's legs. Bend the top hip up and rotate it slightly forward. Place a pillow lengthwise between the resident's knees to separate their legs down to their ankles.

Finish with the following steps:

☐ Determine the resident's preferred position for comfort and ask them if they need anything else.

☐ Examine the environment for safety and cleanliness.

☐ Secure the call light and any other needed items within reach of the resident.

☐ Perform hand hygiene.

☐ Document the procedure and report any findings to the staff in charge.

_____ out of _____ = _____ %   Date: _____

Name: _____   Reviewer: _____

Preparing for a New Resident

Does the candidate:

☐ If the room is shared, inform the current resident that there will be a new roommate.

☐ Make sure all the furniture is present and working properly, including the bed, nightstand drawers, over bed table, and bedside chair

☐ Test all call lights to make sure they work? Check over-bed light, bathroom call light systems, and nightlight if present in room and in the bathroom?

☐ Test the TV, if present.

☐ Assemble the room kit used in the facility. This might include:

  ☐ Water pitcher and/or cup (Make sure the resident is allowed to drink water before filling the pitcher.)

  ☐ Soap and washcloth

  ☐ Towel

  ☐ Basin

  ☐ Lotion and mouthwash

  ☐ Emesis basin

  ☐ Toothbrush and toothpaste

☐ Find out if any special medical equipment, such as an IV stand, O2, bedside commode, or special bed are needed.

☐ Make the bed, and fold the sheets and blankets neatly downward to open the bed.

☐ Make the bed and room welcoming.

_____ out of _____ = _____ %

Date: _____

Name: _____

Reviewer: _____

Does the candidate:

☐ Check care plan

☐ Knock, introduce self, and address resident by preferred name.

☐ Perform hand hygiene.

☐ Gather equipment and secure assistance if needed:

☐ Explain procedure and ask about resident preferences.

☐ Respect privacy and rights at all times.

Continue with the following steps:

☐ Move the resident to the opposite side of the bed from that onto which you intend to roll the resident.

☐ Tuck one arm close to the body.

☐ Cross outside leg over the body, and roll the resident onto the stomach, following through with the hips and then the shoulders. If a catheter is in place, a flat pillow under the abdomen will help keep the pressure off of the catheter.

☐ Gently free the arm from under the body and position it behind the body.

☐ Adjust the head pillow.

☐ Replace the hand rolls and ankle pillows or foam.

☐ Apply lotion and gently massage the feet.

☐ Cover resident with top sheet, and adjust resident position for comfort.

Finish with the following steps:

☐ Determine the resident's preferred position for comfort and ask them if they need anything else.

☐ Examine the environment for safety and cleanliness.

☐ Secure the call light and any other needed items within reach of the resident.

☐ Perform hand hygiene.

☐ Document the procedure and report any findings to the staff in charge.

_____ out of _____ = _____ %   Date: _____

Name: _____   Reviewer: _____

Competency Checklist

Range of Motion Exercises to Lower Extremities

Does the candidate:

☐ Check care plan

☐ Knock, introduce self, and address resident by preferred name.

☐ Perform hand hygiene.

☐ Gather equipment and secure assistance if needed:

☐ Explain procedure and ask about resident preferences.

☐ Respect privacy and rights at all times.

Continue with the following steps:

Each exercise should be performed five to 10 times, depending on the resident's comfort level and ability. Start with the hip and work your way down to the foot.

HIP

☐ Place one hand under the thigh and the other hand below the knee around the calf. Adjust your hand placement as needed to be comfortable for both you and the resident.

☐ Help the resident bring their leg up toward the chest with the knee bent (flexion).

☐ Bring the leg back down toward the bed (extension)

☐ Help the resident move their leg out to the side (abduction).

☐ Bring the leg back toward the other leg (adduction).

☐ Help the resident bring the leg partly up toward the chest with the knee bent. Now gently turn the leg in (internal rotation) and out (external rotation).

KNEE

☐ Place one hand above the resident's knee, under or on their thigh. Place the other hand below their knee around the calf.

☐ Help the resident bend the leg up toward the chest slightly. From this position, help them bend the knee (flexion).

☐ With the hip in the same position as described above, help the resident straighten the knee (extension).

ANKLE

☐ Place one hand above the resident's ankle around the lower part of the calf. Place the other hand around the bottom of their foot.

☐ Help the resident bend the foot up toward the head while the knee is held straight (dorsiflexion), and then point the foot downward (plantar flexion).

☐ Help the resident turn the bottom of the foot outward (eversion) and then inward (inversion).

FOOT

☐ Place your fingers around each of the resident's toes and gently bend (flexion) and straighten each toe at each of the joints (extension).

☐ You can also bend and straighten all the toes at once.

Finish with the following steps:

☐ Determine the resident's preferred position for comfort and ask them if they need anything else.

☐ Examine the environment for safety and cleanliness.

☐ Secure the call light and any other needed items within reach of the resident.

☐ Perform hand hygiene.

☐ Document the procedure and report any findings to the staff in charge.

_____ out of _____ = _____ %   Date: _____

Name: _____   Reviewer: _____

Competency Checklist

Range of Motion Exercises to Upper Extremities

Does the candidate:

☐ Check care plan

☐ Knock, introduce self, and address resident by preferred name.

☐ Perform hand hygiene.

☐ Gather equipment and secure assistance if needed:

☐ Explain procedure and ask about resident preferences.

☐ Respect privacy and rights at all times.

Continue with the following steps:

SHOULDER, ARM, AND HAND

Each exercise should be performed five to 10 times, depending on the resident's comfort level and ability. Start with the shoulder and work your way down to the hand. For each exercise, help the resident move the joint or move it yourself, depending on how much they can do independently.

SHOULDER

☐ Place one hand under the resident's elbow and the other under their wrist. Allow the resident's forearm to rest on your body as you move the arm. If the resident is on their back, stand close to the side of the arm you are moving.

☐ Help the resident to lift their arm up toward the head of the bed with the elbow straight (flexion).

☐ Bring the arm back down to the bed (extension).

☐ Help the resident lift their arm out to the side with the elbow straight (abduction).

☐ Bring the arm back toward the side (adduction).

☐ Help the resident lift their arm halfway out to the side. With the elbow bent, rotate the arm down (internal rotation) and up (external rotation).

ELBOW

☐ Place one hand above the resident's elbow, and use your other hand to support the wrist. The wrist position should be neutral, not bent forward or backward.

☐ Help the resident bend the elbow by bringing the hand toward the upper arm with the palm facing up (flexion).

☐ Help the resident straighten the elbow by bringing the hand down toward the bed until the elbow is as straight as possible (extension).

☐ Help the resident turn the palm over with the elbow fairly straight and the wrist neutral (pronation).

☐ Help the resident turn the palm back up with the elbow fairly straight and the wrist neutral (supination).

WRIST

☐ Place one hand around the resident's forearm just above the wrist and your other hand in their hand.

Competency Checklist
Range of Motion Exercises to Upper Extremities Cont.

☐ Help the resident bend their wrist down (flexion)

☐ Help the resident bend their wrist back (extension).

☐ Help the resident move their hand toward the little finger side of the wrist (ulnar deviation).

☐ Help the resident move their hand toward the thumb side of the wrist (radial deviation).

HAND

☐ Using your fingers, help the resident move their fingers one by one. Bend and straighten each finger at each of the creases (joints).

☐ Curl the hand into a fist, then straighten the fingers back out (flexion and extension).

☐ Spread the fingers away from each other one at a time (abduction) and then back together one at a time (adduction).

☐ Bring each finger across the palm to the thumb and back out (opposition).

Finish with the following steps:

☐ Determine the resident's preferred position for comfort and ask them if they need anything else.

☐ Examine the environment for safety and cleanliness.

☐ Secure the call light and any other needed items within reach of the resident.

☐ Perform hand hygiene.

☐ Document the procedure and report any findings to the staff in charge.

_____ out of _____ = _____ %   Date: _____

Name: _____   Reviewer: _____

Competency Checklist
Shampooing and Conditioning

Does the candidate:

☐ Check care plan.

☐ Knock, introduce self, and address resident by preferred name.

☐ Perform hand hygiene.

☐ Gather equipment and secure assistance if needed:

    ☐ Washcloth

    ☐ Comb and brush

    ☐ Shampoo

    ☐ Conditioner, if used

    ☐ Shampoo trough or basin, if needed

    ☐ 1 to 3 towels

    ☐ Waterproof bed protector, if needed

☐ Explain procedure and ask about resident preferences

☐ Respect privacy and rights at all times.

Continue with the following steps:

☐ Help the resident into a chair, if not having hair washed in bed.

☐ Comb or brush out any tangles before shampooing.

☐ Turn on the water to a warm temperature. The water temperature should be 98.6°F to 100°F. You can use a thermometer if one is available, or test the water temperature with the inside of your wrist. After you do this, have the resident feel the water to be sure it is comfortable.

☐ Help the resident take off their clothes for showering or tub bathing. Wash the resident's hair first or last, as the resident prefers.

☐ If a resident is shampooing at the sink, put the back of the chair against the front of the sink. Pad the rim of the sink with a towel. Position the resident for the method you are using: upright in a shower chair, flat in bed with pillows placed under the shoulders, or tilted in shampoo chair. Protect the resident's clothes with a towel draped over the shoulders. If you are shampooing in bed, you need a shampoo trough, basin, or pail, and a waterproof bed protector.

☐ Place a washcloth over the resident's eyes to prevent shampoo or water from getting into the eyes.

☐ Wet the hair entirely. Pour a small amount of shampoo into your palm and apply it to the resident's wet hair. Massage the shampoo gently throughout hair and scalp. Some residents use special shampoos or conditioners, which may be prescribed to treat a specific condition. Ask the nurse for instructions and read the labels carefully before using these products.

☐ Rinse the hair well with warm water.

☐ Apply conditioner, if used.

☐ Rinse the hair well with warm water.

☐ Help the resident out of the shower or tub into the chair and cover with a bath blanket. Wrap a towel around the hair.

☐ Help the resident dry off and get dressed.

☐ If the resident is in bed, help them wipe their face with the cloth used to protect their eyes. Remove the trough or basin and remove the waterproof pad. Change the linen as necessary. Position the resident with the head of the bed up.

☐ Dry the hair thoroughly and quickly to prevent chilling. Use a hair dryer on a low setting.

☐ Style the resident's hair as they prefer. Check the scalp for any flaking, reddened areas, or other problems. Perform hand hygiene.

☐ Help the resident back to their room. Bring any personal hygiene products back to the room, as well.

Finish with the following steps:

☐ Determine the resident's preferred position for comfort and ask them if they need anything else.

☐ Examine the environment for safety and cleanliness.

☐ Secure the call light and any other needed items within reach of the resident.

☐ Perform hand hygiene.

☐ Document the procedure and report any findings to the staff in charge.

_____ out of _____ = _____ %   Date: _____

Name: _____   Reviewer: _____

Shaving a Male Resident's Face

Does the candidate:

☐ Check care plan.

☐ Knock, introduce self, and address resident by preferred name.

☐ Perform hand hygiene.

☐ Gather equipment and secure assistance if needed:

    ☐ Gloves   ☐ Basin half filled with warm water   ☐ Washcloth

    ☐ Safety razor   ☐ Towel   ☐ Mirror

☐ Explain procedure and ask about resident preferences.

☐ Respect privacy and rights at all times.

Continue with the following steps:

☐ Observe the resident's face for any moles, rashes, or cuts. Do not shave those areas and use extra care if you do.

☐ Place a towel over the resident's chest to protect his clothing.

☐ Put on gloves.

☐ Using a washcloth, wet the beard with warm water. Apply shaving cream with your hands.

☐ When the beard is covered with shaving cream and softened, begin shaving. Shave in the direction the beard grows. Hold the skin taut and smooth by pulling the skin upward with one hand and shaving with a downward stroke with your other hand. Use short, even strokes. Be particularly careful with the neck, chin, and upper lip. Use upward strokes for the neck, downward and slightly diagonal strokes for the chin, and very short downward strokes above the lip.

☐ Rinse the razor in warm water after each stroke.

☐ Rinse the resident's face with the washcloth, dry his face, and apply aftershave liquid or lotion, if he prefers.

☐ Remove towel from the resident's chest.

☐ Remove gloves and perform hand hygiene.

☐ Give the resident a mirror to view his face to make sure he is satisfied with his appearance.

Finish with the following steps:

☐ Determine the resident's preferred position for comfort and ask them if they need anything else.

☐ Examine the environment for safety and cleanliness.

☐ Secure the call light and any other needed items within reach of the resident.

☐ Perform hand hygiene.

☐ Document the procedure and report any findings to the staff in charge.

_____ out of _____ = _____ %   Date: _____

Name: _____   Reviewer: _____

Competency Checklist
Shaving a Male Resident's Face Using an Electric Razor

Does the candidate:

☐ Check care plan.

☐ Knock, introduce self, and address resident by preferred name.

☐ Perform hand hygiene.

☐ Gather equipment and secure assistance if needed:

☐ Gloves   ☐ Basin half filled with warm water   ☐ Washcloth

☐ Electric Razor   ☐ Towel   ☐ Mirror

☐ Explain procedure and ask about resident preferences.

☐ Respect privacy and rights at all times

Continue with the following steps:

☐ Observe the resident's face for any moles, rashes, or cuts. Do not shave those areas, or use extra care if you do.

☐ Place a towel over the resident's chest to protect his clothing.

☐ Put on gloves.

☐ Pull the skin taut and begin shaving the resident's face and neck. Shave using circular motions when using a rotary razor. For foil razors, use a back and forth motion in the direction the beard grows.

☐ Rinse the resident's face with the washcloth, dry his face, and apply aftershave liquid or lotion, if he prefers.

☐ Remove the towel from the resident's chest.

☐ Remove gloves and perform hand hygiene.

☐ Give the resident a mirror to view his face to make sure he is satisfied with his appearance.

☐ Clean the razor according to the manufacturer's guidelines.

Finish with the following steps:

☐ Determine the resident's preferred position for comfort and ask them if they need anything else.

☐ Examine the environment for safety and cleanliness.

☐ Secure the call light and any other needed items within reach of the resident.

☐ Perform hand hygiene.

☐ Document the procedure and report any findings to the staff in charge.

_____ out of _____ = _____ %   Date: _____

Name: _____   Reviewer: _____

Competency Checklist

Shower

Does the candidate:

☐ Check care plan.

☐ Knock, introduce self, and address resident by preferred name.

☐ Perform hand hygiene.

☐ Gather equipment and secure assistance if needed:

☐ Gloves

☐ At least 3 towels

☐ At least 2 washcloths

☐ Shower cap (if needed)

☐ Shower chair (if needed)

☐ Bath blanket

☐ Bath mat

☐ Soap, lotion, shampoo, etc.

☐ Resident's clothing of choice

☐ Explain procedure and ask about resident preferences.

☐ Respect privacy and rights at all times.

Continue with the following steps:

☐ Help the resident to the shower room/area and bring all necessary supplies.

☐ Help the resident sit on the shower chair.

☐ Turn on the shower and run with warm water. The water temperature should be 98.6°F to 100°F. You can use a thermometer if one is available, or test the water temperature with the inside of your wrist. After you do this, have the resident feel the water to be sure it is comfortable. Adjust the temperature as needed.

☐ Help the resident remove his or her clothing.

☐ Help the resident into the shower. Encourage the use of safety rails. Most facilities have shower chairs that lock in place. If the resident needs to shower in a seated position, be sure the shower chair is locked before they sit down.

☐ If the resident is not shampooing, use a shower cap to protect hair from getting wet.

☐ Help the resident with showering as needed. (Wear gloves if you help with perineal care.) Encourage the resident to participate as much as possible. Give help and verbal cues as needed. Wash from head to toe. Rinse the washcloth as needed. Provide clean washcloth to cleanse perineal area.

☐ Place a dry towel on the chair outside the shower.

☐ Turn off the shower. Turn off the hot water first to prevent a burn.

☐ Help the resident out of the shower and onto the covered chair. Cover the resident with a bath blanket.

☐ Help the resident dry off, use personal hygiene products, and get dressed.

☐ You may give a back rub before dressing, if the resident desires. Perform hand hygiene.

☐ Help the resident back to their room. Bring any personal hygiene products back to the room.

Finish with the following steps:

☐ Determine the resident's preferred position for comfort and ask them if they need anything else.

☐ Examine the environment for safety and cleanliness.

☐ Secure the call light and any other needed items within reach of the resident.

☐ Perform hand hygiene.

☐ Document the procedure and report any findings to the staff in charge.

_____ out of _____ = _____ %   Date: _____

Name: _____   Reviewer: _____

Competency Checklist
Taking a Manual Blood Pressure

Does the candidate:

☐ Check the care plan.

☐ Knock, introduce self, and address resident by preferred name.

☐ Perform hand hygiene.

☐ Gather supplies and secure assistance if needed:

    ☐ Alcohol wipes

    ☐ Stethoscope

    ☐ Sphygmomanometer with cuff of correct size for resident

☐ Explain procedure and ask about resident preferences.

☐ Respect privacy and rights at all times.

Continue with the following steps:

☐ Have the resident place one arm on the bed, bedside table, or arm of a chair, with the palm facing up and elbow at the same level as the heart. (If the arm is higher than the heart, the blood pressure can register too low. If the arm is lower than the heart, the blood pressure can register too high.)

☐ Expose the resident's arm by rolling the sleeve up to the shoulder, taking care that the sleeve is not too tight on the arm, which could increase the blood pressure.

☐ Wrap the blood pressure cuff evenly around the upper arm 1 inch above the elbow. Be sure to use the correct size cuff. The wrong size cuff can result in an incorrect reading. The cuff should fit over the center of the resident's upper arm. It should not extend to the elbow or under the resident's armpit.

☐ Make sure that the resident's extended arm is not lying on the tubing and that the tubing is not kinked. The tube attached to the bulb should be on the side closest to the resident's body. The tube to the sphygmomanometer gauge should be on the other side of the arm, away from the body.

☐ Close the valve (small metal knob on the bulb) in the air pump by turning it clockwise.

☐ Place the stethoscope earpieces in your ears.

☐ Locate the pulsation in the brachial artery by placing your second and third fingers over the area. When you find the pulse, place the diaphragm of the stethoscope firmly over the area and hold it in place with your left hand. (Do this with your right hand if you are left-handed.)

☐ With your right hand (left, if left-handed), pump air into the cuff by squeezing the bulb until the gauge measures 180–200. If you hear the pulse as soon as you stop pumping, begin again and pump the cuff pressure so the gauge reads higher than 200.

☐ Slowly open the valve on the bulb and watch the cuff pressure decrease on the gauge.

☐ Listen for the first thumping sound and note the pressure reading; this number is the systolic pressure.

☐ Continue to listen for a distinct change in sound (a muffled sound) or the last sound and note the pressure reading; this number is the diastolic pressure.

☐ Record the results.

Finish with the following steps:

☐ Determine the resident's preferred position for comfort and ask them if they need anything else.

☐ Examine the environment for safety and cleanliness.

☐ Secure the call light and any other needed items within reach of the resident.

☐ Document the procedure and report any findings to the staff in charge.

_____ out of _____ = _____ %   Date: _____

Name: _____   Reviewer: _____

Competency Checklist
Taking an Oral Temperature With an Electronic Thermometer

Does the candidate:

☐ Check the care plan.

☐ Gather supplies and secure assistance if needed.

    ☐ Electronic thermometer

    ☐ Gloves, if needed

☐ Perform hand hygiene?

☐ Knock, introduce self, and address resident by preferred name.?

☐ Explain procedure and ask about resident preferences.

☐ Respect privacy and rights at all times.

Continue with the following steps:

☐ First, check with the resident to make sure that they have not consumed anything hot or cold or smoked within the last 10 minutes. If they have, wait 5 to 10 minutes before proceeding.

☐ Put on gloves if there is a possibility of contact with body fluids.

☐ Ensure that the thermometer is reset, and then put on the plastic probe cover.

☐ Insert the thermometer probe under the resident's tongue, and ask them to close their lips around it. Do not allow the resident to walk while the thermometer.

☐ Wait for the signal (beep) that the temperature reading is complete. As you wait you can take the resident's pulse and respiratory rates.

☐ Remove the thermometer and the plastic cover. If here is an excessive amount of mucus on the thermometer when you remove it, use gloves or another barrier to remove the cover if necessary.

☐ Read the temperature and record the result.

Finish with the following steps:

☐ Determine the resident's preferred position for comfort and ask them if they need anything else.

☐ Examine the environment for safety and cleanliness.

☐ Secure the call light and any other needed items within reach of the resident.

☐ Perform hand hygiene.

☐ Document the procedure and report any findings to the staff in charge.

_____ out of _____ = _____ %   Date: _____

Name: _____   Reviewer: _____

Taking a Radial Pulse

Does the candidate:

☐ Check the care plan.

☐ Knock, introduce self, and address resident by preferred name.

☐ Perform hand hygiene.

☐ Gather supplies and secure assistance if needed.

    ☐ Watch with a second hand

☐ Explain procedure and ask about resident preferences.

☐ Respect privacy and rights at all times.

Continue with the following steps:

☐ Place your second and third fingers on thumb side of client's wrist to locate radial pulse.

☐ Look at your watch, and when the second hand is on the 12, start counting the pulse for one minute. Count each beat you feel. Check for abnormalities in the rhythm.

☐ Record the result.

Finish with the following steps:

☐ Determine the resident's preferred position for comfort and ask them if they need anything else.

☐ Examine the environment for safety and cleanliness.

☐ Secure the call light and any other needed items within reach of the resident.

☐ Perform hand hygiene.

☐ Document the procedure and report any findings to the staff in charge.

_____ out of _____ = _____ %   Date: _____

Name: _____   Reviewer: _____

Competency Checklist
Taking a Respiratory Rate

Does the candidate:

☐ Check the care plan.

☐ Knock, introduce self, and address resident by preferred name.

☐ Perform hand hygiene.

☐ Gather supplies and secure assistance if needed.

    ☐ Watch with a second hand

☐ Explain procedure and ask about resident preferences.

☐ Respect privacy and rights at all times.

Continue with the following steps:

☐ Count the respiratory rate immediately after counting the pulse rate.

☐ Keep your fingers on the resident's radial pulse but without pressure. You do this so the resident will breathe normally.

☐ Watch the chest go up with inspiration and down with expiration. Count the respiratory rate for one minute

☐ Record the result.

Finish with the following steps:

☐ Determine the resident's preferred position for comfort and ask them if they need anything else.

☐ Examine the environment for safety and cleanliness.

☐ Secure the call light and any other needed items within reach of the resident.

☐ Perform hand hygiene.

☐ Document the procedure and report any findings to the staff in charge.

_____ out of _____ = _____ %   Date: _____

Name: _____   Reviewer: _____

Transferring from a Bed to a Wheelchair (Stand-Pivot Transfer)

Does the candidate:

☐ Check care plan.

☐ Knock, introduce self, and address resident by preferred name.

☐ Perform hand hygiene.

☐ Gather equipment and secure assistance if needed:

☐ Explain procedure and ask about resident preferences.

☐ Respect privacy and rights at all times.

Continue with the following steps:

☐ Position wheelchair close to bed with arm of the wheelchair almost touching the bed.

☐ Stand in front of the resident. If a wheelchair is the target, make sure that its wheels are locked and the leg rests are out of the way or removed. Ensure that the resident has on non slip footwear. Apply gait belt unless contraindicated.

☐ Place one of your legs between the resident's legs and the other close to the chair or wheelchair. (This gives you better control over the speed and the direction of the movement.)

☐ Hold onto the gait belt at the resident's back, slightly to one side. If you are not using a gait belt, wrap your arms around the resident's waist.

☐ Ask the resident to push down on the bed with their hands, lean forward, and stand up. If the resident cannot push off of the bed, you can have them hold onto your waist during the transfer. Do not let the resident hold you around your neck because it places you at risk for injury.

☐ On the count of three, help the resident stand by leaning your body back and up, bringing the resident's body forward. Ask them to lean forward and stand up.

☐ Once the resident is standing, keep your back neutral and body facing forward. Pivot (turning your feet or taking small steps) to turn them until the backs of their knees are against the chair.

☐ Ask the resident to reach back for the arm of the chair with one or both hands, if possible.

☐ Help the resident bend their knees and sit.

☐ Once the resident is seated, ask then to push back in the chair by pushing down with their feet on the floor and arms on the armrests. If they cannot do this, you will need to help them move back in the chair. Remove gait belt and position feet on the leg rests.

Finish with the following steps:

☐ Determine the resident's preferred position for comfort and ask them if they need anything else.

☐ Examine the environment for safety and cleanliness.

☐ Secure the call light and any other needed items within reach of the resident.

☐ Perform hand hygiene.

☐ Document the procedure and report any findings to the staff in charge.

_____ out of _____ = _____ %   Date: _____

Name: _____   Reviewer: _____

Competency Checklist
Tub Bath

Does the candidate:

☐ Check care plan.

☐ Knock, introduce self, and address resident by preferred name.

☐ Perform hand hygiene.

☐ Gather equipment and secure assistance if needed:

    ☐ Gloves

    ☐ At least 3 towels

    ☐ At least 2 washcloths

    ☐ Soap, lotion, shampoo, etc.

    ☐ Shower chair (if needed)

    ☐ Bath mat

    ☐ Bath blanket

    ☐ Resident's clothing of choice

☐ Explain procedure and ask about resident preferences.

☐ Respect privacy and rights at all times.

Continue with the following steps:

☐ Assist the resident to the tub room and bring all necessary supplies. Some facilities may use chairs on wheels to transport residents to the tub room. Make sure that the resident is properly dressed and draped to protect their privacy. Use the safety straps if needed and available.

☐ Help the resident sit on the chair. Fill the tub halfway with warm water.

☐ Remember, always turn off the hot water first. The water temperature should be 98.6°F to 100°F. You can use a thermometer if one is available, or test the water temperature with the inside of your wrist. After you do this, have the resident feel the water to be sure it is comfortable. The resident's physician may order special additives to the bath water, such as bran, oatmeal, starch, sodium bicarbonate, Epsom salts, pine products, sulfa, potassium permanganate, or salt. Always check with the charge nurse about the proper use of any of these substances.

☐ Help the resident remove his or her clothing.

☐ Check that the bath mat is in place. Help the resident into the tub.

☐ Help with bathing as needed. (Put on gloves if you will be assisting with perineal care.) Provide washcloth to cleanse body area; the second washcloth will be used to clean perineal area. Never leave the resident alone in a tub. Always encourage residents to use safety rails. Be sure to check the water temperature during the tub bath to be sure it has not become too cold. Add hot water as needed, not allowing water to run directly on the resident to prevent burns.

☐ Place a clean towel on the seat of the chair.

☐ Help the resident out of the tub, encouraging the use of safety rails. Cover the resident with a bath blanket.

☐ Help the resident with drying, applying personal hygiene products, and dressing.

☐ You may give a back rub before dressing, if the resident desires. Remove gloves, if used, and perform hand hygiene.

☐ Help the resident back to their room. Bring any personal hygiene products back to the room.

Finish with the following steps:

☐ Determine the resident's preferred position for comfort and ask them if they need anything else.

☐ Examine the environment for safety and cleanliness.

☐ Secure the call light and any other needed items within reach of the resident.

☐ Perform hand hygiene.

☐ Document the procedure and report any findings to the staff in charge.

_____ out of _____ = _____ %   Date: _____

Name: _____   Reviewer: _____

Competency Checklist
Urinary Catheter Care

Does the candidate:

☐ Check care plan

☐ Knock, introduce self, and address resident by preferred name.

☐ Perform hand hygiene.

☐ Gather equipment and secure assistance if needed:

    ☐ Gloves   ☐ Soap and water

    ☐ At least 2 washcloths   ☐ Towels

☐ Explain procedure and ask about resident preferences.

☐ Respect privacy and rights at all times.

Continue with the following steps:

☐ Put on gloves

☐ Pull back top sheet, only exposing area to be cleaned.

☐ Always keep the external catheter tube as clean as possible.

☐ Clean the tubing with soap and water and a washcloth. Clean the tube first at the urethral opening, and then cleanse downward and away from the opening. To prevent discomfort for the resident, do not pull on the catheter tube while cleaning it.

☐ Use a clean area of the washcloth for each downward stroke.

☐ Do the rest of perineal care as usual, cleansing with soap and water from front to back.

☐ Check the tubing for kinks and leaks.

☐ The urinary drainage bag is secured to the bed or chair below the resident's bladder, so that the urine flows downward into the bag by gravity. Never let the drainage bag touch the floor, which is considered an unclean area. Never lift the drainage bag above the resident because urine could flow back into the bladder, increasing the risk of infection.

☐ When you help a resident with a catheter change position, follow these guidelines: The external part of the catheter tube can be secured with a strap to the resident's upper thigh to prevent pulling on the catheter when they move. The urinary catheter tube, connecting tube, and drainage bag should not be separated except by a nurse using a sterile technique to change the tubing or collect a specimen. The drainage system is kept closed to help prevent infection.

☐ Remove gloves and perform hand hygiene.

☐ Replace top sheet over resident.

Finish with the following steps:

☐ Determine the resident's preferred position for comfort and ask them if they need anything else.

☐ Examine the environment for safety and cleanliness.

☐ Secure the call light and any other needed items within reach of the resident.

☐ Perform hand hygiene.

☐ Document the procedure and report any findings to the staff in charge.

_____ out of _____ = _____ %   Date: _____

Name: _____   Reviewer: _____